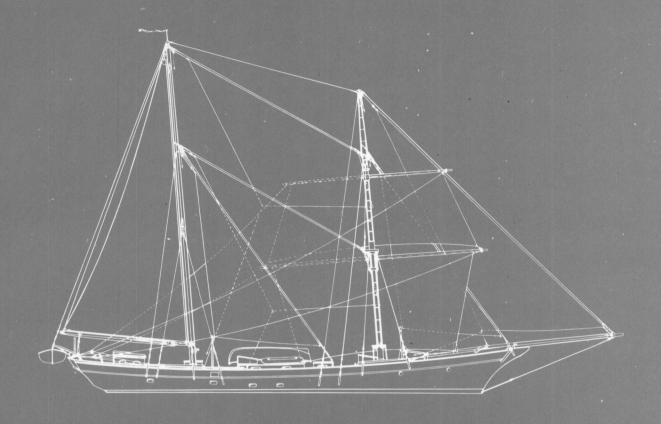

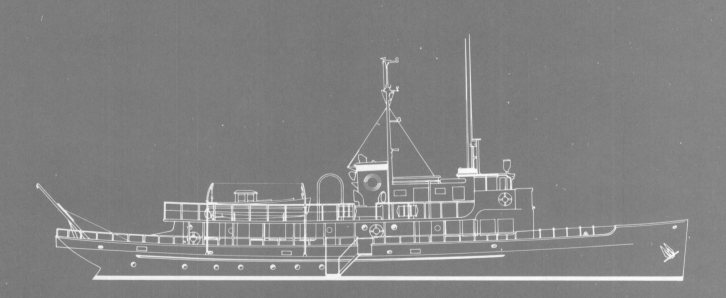

VOYAGING
WITH THE
WHALES

VOYAGING WITH THE WHALES

Cynthia D'Vincent
with Delphine Haley and Fred A. Sharpe
Introduction by Jim Fowler

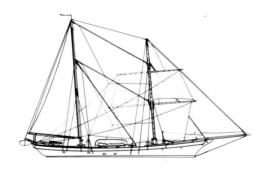

Oakwell Boulton

Chicago Toronto

This book is dedicated to Storm and Eve.

My two young children, Storm and Eve, are really
a very large part of this book. From the time they
were born they have joined us on our research
voyages. Many of the photographs were taken
while one peered over my shoulder from a back-
pack or slept on my chest in a Snugli, or both.
Though always awestruck by the magnificence of
the whales, they have over the years come to
know the subtleties of the behaviors and now
have refreshing perspectives to offer. There is
nothing so poignant as the innocent questions of a
child to keep an omniscient attitude in check,
particularly when it concerns an animal as mysterious as the humpback whale.

C.D'V.

©1989 Boulton Publishing Services Inc., Toronto
ISBN 0-920831-09-5   First Edition

Designed by Falcom Design and Communications Inc., Toronto

Produced and published by Boulton Publishing Services Inc., Toronto

Printed and bound in Hong Kong by Book Art Inc., Toronto

Library of Congress Cataloging-in-Publication Data

D'Vincent, Cynthia. 1950–
    Voyaging with the whales / Cynthia D'Vincent
with Delphine Haley and Fred A. Sharpe :
introduction by Jim Fowler. — 1st ed.
        p.   cm.
    Bibliography: p.
    Includes index.
    ISBN 0-920831-09-5 : $39.95
    1. Humpback whale—Behavior. I. Haley,
Delphine. II. Sharpe, Fred. III. Title.
QL737.C424D85 1989   89-9465
599.5'1—dc20   CIP

1 Breaching (frontispiece) *Adult humpback
breaches in Frederick Sound.*

CONTENTS

LIST OF PLATES

(short titles only – fuller descriptions accompany plates)

ACKNOWLEDGEMENTS

I wish to express my deep gratitude to those people who helped to bring this book about. My husband Russ Nilson has worked with me during every facet of the research. It is his vision and his remarkable energy that have made Intersea Research and consequently our field work even possible at all. I should like to thank Delphine Haley for her contributions and her review of the manuscript, and Fred Sharpe for his assistance in the preparation of the scientific text. I also thank Dale Rice and Allen Wolman at the National Marine Mammal Laboratory of the National Marine Fisheries Service, Dr. Chris Clark of Cornell University, Dr. Steve Katona of the College of the Atlantic, and Ken Balcomb of the Center for Whale Research, for their critical reviews and valuable commentaries on the scientific text. Finally my thanks go to those many people, from all walks of life, who took part in our expeditions over the years and thereby supported these studies.

Cynthia D'Vincent, Intersea Research,
Friday Harbor, Washington 98250.

Photographic Credits

©Russ Nilson
Plates 4, 46

©Frans Lanting
Plate 18

©Deborah Glockner-Ferrari/Center for Whale Studies
Plates 38, 40

©Kenneth C. Balcomb III
Plate 39

©Fred A. Sharpe
Plate 98, 104, and line drawing of whale

©Jane Yamaguchi
Plate 113

©Cynthia D'Vincent
All other photographs

INTRODUCTION
by Jim Fowler

The first sight of a great whale is one of life's most intense experiences, especially for a zoologist. To me this came in Alaska, when I went there to join Cynthia D'Vincent and her husband Russ Nilson on board their ship *Acania*. We were to film the story of their research work among the humpback whales. This was to be for the television show, "Mutual of Omaha's Wild Kingdom".

We were standing together on the forward deck of the vessel, not far from shore. Mist hung in the air above a calm and silent sea. All around us rose the breathtaking scenery of that most magnificent part of the world, and I gazed upon it while we waited for the whales.

Few places on earth are so spectacular as the southeast coast of Alaska. The southern tip of Chile, and the west coast of New Zealand's South Island, may perhaps come close in comparison of beauty, but even they lack the incredible range of features and life forms to be found in that part of Alaska. Spectacular waterfalls cascading down the 3000-foot high walls of the fjords are backed by snow-covered peaks. Islands of primeval forest are looked upon by gigantic glaciers that extend from the mountains to the sea. The weather incessantly changes. Rain and storm will give way to a fantastic sunset that looks like a fiery celebration of the closing day.

No less dramatic, rich and intriguing, is the wildlife. Eagles, falcons, sea birds, land and marine mammals are all the time to be seen. At any moment you expect a moose or a grizzly bear to break out of the forest or come round a bend of the shore. The waters are dark with plankton, on which feed enormous schools of fish that in turn support a long and complex but still healthy food chain. All this together is awesome. There is a sense of wonder, of mystery about the place. I stood on the deck of *Acania*, held in suspense, waiting for something to happen.

Suddenly the surface erupted less than sixty yards away. An immense black shape surged straight up, fifty feet out of the water, hung in the air as though hesitating, then crashed back down to the surface again with a thunderclap that echoed among the hills.

The whole performance lasted but a moment. Shockwaves raced across the water, signalling the force and impact of the breach, then just as suddenly all was silent, and ahead of us came the rest of the pod of whales, slow and deliberate, periodically surfacing, puffing and blowing like a parade of old steam engines slightly out of sync with one another. It was strange to realize that down below the surface of these still waters were such enormous animals that could from one moment to another be so boisterous and then again so tranquil.

This first sight of a breaching whale put me in mind of the first time I had seen elephants in the wild. It was on a misty morning in Africa after a night filled with tumult.

Daybreak revealed unmistakable signs that elephants had passed by my camp in the dark. A jagged swath trampled through the forest marked their route, no less than sixty feet wide. Large trees and bushes were twisted, uprooted and torn, as though a bulldozer had just been through to make a road. I found it hard to imagine animals large enough to do this, but there they were, and I hurried to see them, led by the sound of trumpeting in the distance as the herd continued to feed.

That was another thing about the whales—the trumpeting! I was astounded to hear it—a sound so much like the trumpet call of elephants. Amazing, and totally unexpected, these clarion bellowings from the ocean. It was almost as though the humpback whales were elephants of the deep.

Just as the elephants are important to the forest system as, by their trampling down of the dense growth, they let in sunlight to stimulate new food for smaller animals, so the humpback whales in their ways must be an essential part of the oceanic ecosystems on which all life depends. In the early days of the environmental movement we inadvertently set the needs of animals and humans apart, in two separate camps, at least so far as public perceptions were concerned. We can't afford to do that again. We're all in it together now.

I was remembering and pondering all this as *Acania* started to glide steadily through the water again, quietly keeping pace with the whales. What were they really doing, I wondered, and why did they do one thing this day, another the next? How did they migrate, finding their ways

2   Fluking and blowing
Acania *and* Varua *in the background.*

twice a year across thousands of miles of ocean? Why did
they sing their long and haunting songs? Why did they
breach? How did they feed together? What kind of
relationships did they have among themselves? So many
questions came to mind.

It is to answer such questions that Cynthia D'Vincent
and Russ Nilson have chosen to devote their lives to
studying this most dramatic member of the animal
kingdom. As Cynthia herself is ever ready to say, our
knowledge of the whales is only at the beginning. There is

so much we have yet to understand. And the situation is urgent. This research is timely. Commercial interests are threatening an ecosystem so delicate and so interdependen that small changes can suddenly result in large disasters. Because the whales are at the summit of the food-chain, they are the prime indicator of the health of the environment. If they can survive, then everything else can survive in turn but if, for example, logging, mining, overfishing, excessive marine traffic, or any other such intrusions, should alter the mineral composition of the water, cause silting by way of erosion, pollution by human encroachment, or interfere by noise and other disturbance, then the food organisms and ultimately the whales themselves will be lost, before we even know the meaning of behaviors like their songs, let alone the history and significance of their multi-million-year existence.

Whales are part of the ocean and the ocean, according to some schools of thought, is our "lifeblood". The health of the oceans is critical to the health of all species and so to our own survival. We are only just now beginning to explore below the surface. New knowledge and new thought is beginning to perceive our role less as that of predator and more as that of custodian, clearly connected with whales and all living things in a mutual quest for survival. We can no longer separate their needs from our needs, for it appears that in the long run all needs are the same. Our mission is to discover not just what is here, but how the planet "works". How air, water, forests, open space, foodchains, ecosystems, and all the natural global processes support life, including ours.

It often seems to be the case that for people to feel real concern about a situation they need a sense of personal connection. That is why, in respect of the whales, it is just as important to involve people with them directly as it is to conduct scientific research. And so the kind of expeditions that Cynthia D'Vincent conducts, in which visitors from all walks of life can take part, can be a powerful way of engaging the general public.

Cynthia and Russ are not just limited specialists conducting narrow research. They have lived around the world and know their fellow human beings very well. Conversations at dinner, on the bridge, and during slow days on the boat covered many subjects. Naturally, whales were discussed most frequently. Environment, philosophy, tourism, food, and the future of mankind were probably next, though not necessarily in that order, and all of these subjects seemed to involve the future of whales.

Acania, and *Varua*, their crews and their guests, are altogether unique. Both of the ships are engaged in research. It wouldn't surprise me if Cynthia and Russ purchased and refitted a submarine if they thought it would further the cause of research and help save the humpback! They move through stormy, unpredictable seas one day and calm ones the next. An atmosphere of scientific investigation pervades, surrounded by an encompassing spirit of adventure. You never know when or where the humpbacks will surface. Petite, lightning-fast Dall's porpoises sweep back and forth across the bow, dancing and racing in the waves suddenly coming from nowhere while the search is on. Special underwater recordings of the songs of the whales and other sounds of creatures of the sea are played through a speaker on the bridge. In the evening you can attend a lecture and learn how to identify individual whales known to frequent the area. The white pattern on the tail fluke is often the give-away. It varies in its configuration, just as a human thumbprint does.

This story of research into the habits, movements and needs for survival of the humpback is one that combines all the elements of a real-life drama; intrigue, mystery, danger, high stakes (because the very survival of this great whale is in jeopardy) and exceptional dedication on the part of the researchers as they orchestrate the investigation.

There is no question as to the motive that inspires Cynthia D'Vincent and Russ Nilson. Their guests, their children, and even the ships they captain are all a welcome part of a great adventure, as long as certain goals are met. First, to find out as much about the whales as possible before it is too late, and secondly to share their experience with other people and bring the urgency of the whales' plight to the attention of the world as quickly as possible.

During that time on the *Acania*, there were many memorable events, new thoughts and opportunities to gain new knowledge of the humpbacks. The whales were so spectacular that each day was filled with new adventure. Once, in an inflatable boat called a Zodiac, we were following a pod of whales, trying to record their underwater songs during a particularly spectacular behavior called "lunge feeding". The Zodiac, made famous by Cousteau, is known for its sea-worthiness. All of a sudden, too close for comfort, at least for me, an entire group of ten or eleven of these 50-foot giants came bursting up through the glassy still waters of a cove as if from nowhere. Their maws were wide open, gulping hundreds of pounds of herring in a few seconds before they were gone again, all swallowed up by the sea. Cynthia was calm and cool as usual. After I enquired of her in some detail as to the chance of one of these "lunge feedings" occurring right under the boat, she explained that although she had experienced a few close calls, only once or twice had she almost been capsized!

This reminded me of several near-misses I have had with elephants, grizzlies, sharks and gorillas, but never with whales. Not only did it seem undesirable to end up in the water with humpbacks, but also several groups of killer whales had been seen coursing up and down the channel that day, and even though I know it's said that they don't feed on humans I personally lacked experience in that area, didn't feel like putting the question to the test, and so had a double incentive for not capsizing! The humpbacks usually give away their position a few seconds before they break the surface, with the emergence of a ring of small air bubbles circling the area where the feeding is about to occur. From then on I became very sensitive to the presence of air bubbles anywhere near our Zodiac.

One conversation with Cynthia especially lingers in my mind. It centered around a discussion of the mysterious "cooperative feeding" behavior. Why has this incredible behavior never been observed anywhere else? Not in the Atlantic, the southern oceans or even the other parts of the Pacific. "Cooperative feeding" is a highly structured activity that begins when the whales detect a school of herring. This may be at a considerable distance off, but the whales have extremely sensitive hearing and the school of prey makes a sound in the water as it swims along that some people have likened to a rushing noise or the sound of falling rain. The whale pod leader, often one of the older cows, takes off in the direction of the prey and starts singing a song, and the rest of the pod forms up and follows. We think the song may serve to keep the group in formation or it may stun and disorient the fish. The whales dive under the herring and swimming in circles they blow a net of bubbles that traps the prey and drives them to the surface. All this Cynthia describes and depicts in great detail later on in this book and she draws some remarkable inferences from its implications.

The question that puzzled me was why don't all humpbacks catch fish in this way? Cynthia thought it could be an ancient behavior pattern that had always been handed down from generation to generation. When the humpbacks began to be hunted so mercilessly most of the older and larger individuals were wiped out. Only a few of those that knew the technique survived and these few are now teaching the cooperative behavior to the younger generations. That's why the number of whales who perform this unique activity is on the increase, now that the population is protected.

The research described in this book will give powerful evidence of a well-developed intelligence in whales. The need is not to compare this intelligence with ours, but simply to respect the whales for what they are. More importantly, even before the research is concluded, there is a great challenge before us to affect public opinion and governmental policy as to the importance of the whales to us and our world.

When you glimpse magnificent scenery through weather changes of awesome magnitude the presence of whales adds to the primeval picture of the place. The fjords and coves of southeast Alaska are a perfect setting for the expression of philosophical revelations. One can't resist speculating as to why our species has so thoroughly exploited so many life forms on earth, to the point that now many are facing extinction. We have eaten some, killed off others that were competitive with us, and we seem to judge those that remain only from our more or less selfish human considerations. Our power to destroy, as well as to create, is like the weather, awesome. And yet in the long history of life on our planet, we are such latecomers.

Once years ago, on a slab of tilted limestone in the eastern face of the Rockies near Denver, I stopped beside a road to gaze in wonder at a set of fossilized dinosaur tracks that led up the slope. It was a spellbinding experience. I had always wished that I could see a giant dinosaur and there in front of me quite clearly were the tracks of an adult followed by its young. The mud they had walked through one day in the prehistoric past had turned to stone and here before me now were their marks, as though it had been yesterday. I wondered how many people who drive down that road near Denver know that the tracks are there or would even care.

The humpbacks, cruising in long procession, straight

and methodical down the channel, left me with the same thoughts and feelings. In the case of the whales it is not yet history. But the whales will not leave tracks to be turned to stone, and unless we impress upon the people who cruise Alaskan waters in their yachts and tour boats the significance of what they see, there may someday be no trace left of the whales at all.

Cynthia D'Vincent, more than any other scientist, has lived and worked with this population of humpbacks throughout their range, at their feeding grounds in Alaska, during migration, and at their wintering grounds near Hawaii, where she has studied how they breed and raise their young. Her text and photographs reveal the power and presence of these marine giants as never before. She has lived with the whales, and for the whales, voyaging with them year after year. Her goal has been to learn as much as possible about them, and to share her knowledge with the world. More than a scientist, Cynthia is also an explorer, experiencing high adventure, and calmly confronting danger. She is an authority, one of the few in the world, who is producing answers to these behavioral puzzles. Her work is as vital and as important as what has been done elsewhere on chimpanzees and gorillas. She fully deserves the recognition that she'll receive for this unique and fascinating publication. Making the humpback whale as important to everyone as it is to her is the only way to guarantee its continued existence.

JIM FOWLER
The Explorers' Club New York

3 Feeding (overleaf) *with the baleen plates clearly visible.*

VOYAGING WITH THE WHALES

From earliest times the mammals of the sea have mystified and inspired the imagination of mankind. Yet some of their most extraordinary features have only recently been the subject of scientific study. Their migratory patterns, methods of long-distance navigation, social relationships and leadership roles, the nature and purpose of their songs—these are all aspects of marine mammal behavior that only now begin to be understood. The study of these creatures, so perfectly adapted to the sea, is supremely fascinating and rewarding. As an example, the melodious songs of the humpback whale (*Megaptera novaeangliae*) are among the most lengthy and complex vocalizations to be heard in the animal kingdom, haunting sounds that affect even the most indifferent listener with their beauty, or strike terror, as they have in my own experience when suddenly they herald impending danger. I know of no other sound in nature to compare with them, unless it be that of the whale's blow, which in its timeless serenity may be the most perfect sound of all.

4 Sighting whales (left) *The author sighting whales from the bow of* Varua *(photo by Russ Nilson).*

I first became interested in whales while on a voyage across the South Pacific in the early nineteen seventies. In the Tongan Islands, I spent enough time to become concerned about the 25 whales that inhabited that region. Humpbacks were still being taken by the islanders then, and in a poor economy a 40-foot adult whale, weighing between 30 and 40 tons, could yield as much economically as the slaughter of 50 cattle. It concerned me that the removal of even one whale might be more than this humpback population could stand, and that it would result in a critical loss. Depletion of the gene pool may lead to the extinction of such small populations, but depletion of the information pool may have almost as severe an effect. For example, it is usually the largest whale that is targeted by the hunters; this may be an elder of the whale community and the bearer of significant survival information about critical factors, such as migratory corridors, prey densities of polar feeding areas, and feeding techniques. It may also be a female, since in the mysticetes the females are somewhat larger than the males, and this female may well be pregnant. Or it could be a mother already with calf, which makes it an even easier target. We still know little about the social interaction of whales. We can only say for sure that in a population of 25, if there is no interchange among whales of other island groups, such a small community would have extreme difficulty recovering from the loss of a member, and especially of a bearing female or an elder.

As a result of the concern arising from this Tongan experience, I began to educate myself about southern hemisphere humpback populations and decided to pursue graduate studies in cetology. On my return to the United States, over a year later, I took a job with the National Marine Fisheries Service (NMFS), making a census of the California gray whales on their annual migration. That project led to others, and before long I was on expeditions to remote, exciting and sometimes forbidding lands, working with whales of different species. The gray whale calving lagoons of Baja California were like paradise, with warm winds, total isolation and perhaps more whales in one place than anywhere else in the world. Back in the South Seas again I continued work on the South Pacific humpback stock evaluation in the Cook Islands.

Such studies were always exciting, not only because of the work itself but for the logistics that made such expeditions possible. In the Arctic, research on the endangered bowhead whale had to be conducted from the edge of shorefast ice off Point Barrow, on the North Slope of Alaska, as much as 20 miles from land. The bowhead lives at the edge of the pack-ice, migrating south with the ice in winter and north again in summer, following the lead created as the polar ice cap separates from the shorefast ice. Through this lead travels a wonderful variety of animals, including beluga whales, narwhals and bowheads, as well as seals and thousands of birds. Here, the dangers and discomforts of research were even more apparent. A sheet of ice would break off, taking anyone and anything on it down the lead, or would be driven back up by the wind and buckled into 200-foot high wreckage, crushing camp and campers alike. Polar bears were a silent but ever-present

cause of anxiety. Relationships between the NMFS and the
native peoples were strained when quotas and guidelines
for the whale harvest seemed too restrictive for local
needs. And always, of course, there was the cold, such cold
as I could never have imagined. Yet I spent two
unforgettable springs in the Arctic, and when later I was
invited back by the Alaska Eskimo Whaling Commission I
would have gladly returned to that stark, immense, eerily
beautiful land had not my life with the whales already
taken a slightly different turn.

For a number of years I had been working away at
these varied studies, enjoying the research and the
accompanying excitement. Then, when it seemed that these
adventures would start to wane, I was offered a research
position to investigate the effects of vessel traffic on
humpback whales in Southeast Alaska.

In 1979 a researcher named Chuck Jurasz had noted a
steady decline in the number of humpbacks using Glacier
Bay as a feeding ground, and he had correlated this to the
increasing number of vessels, especially cruise ships, that
were visiting the Bay. NMFS thought a study to assess this
was in order, and I was interested because I had already
done some research on the reactions of whales to vessels in
California. A staff of eight was assembled to work
throughout Frederick Sound, Chatham Strait and Glacier
Bay. Cruise ships would give us information as to their
engine, shaft, and propeller specifics and would on request
change course, speed and direction. Hydrophones
(underwater microphones) would record the sound levels
and frequencies of the ships, and observers would record

the responses of the whales. In addition a systematic study of prey distribution and density would determine the significance of these parameters as a factor in keeping whales faithful to one place.

Our research platform was to be the 93-foot square-rigged brigantine *Varua*, whose beauty and fame were already familiar to me. British naval historian Douglas Phillips-Birt had described her as "the most highly developed and most beautiful ocean-going sailing vessel of her size ever built." When I first saw her myself on arriving in Juneau that summer of 1981, I remembered what the great circumnavigator Eric Hiscock had said when he first saw *Varua*: "The sight of her, even at anchor, was so beautiful that it raised the hair on the back of my neck."

It is said that the gods will not count against our allotted years those that are spent on a sailing ship. Because *Varua* is so much a part of my life, and because without her this book and the research on which it is based would never have been undertaken, it is fitting here to tell a little of her history.

Varua was the dream ship of William A. Robinson, an intrepid mariner who had sailed around the world in 1932 in the smallest boat to have done so at that time—the 32-foot Alden ketch *Svaap*. That voyage and Robinson's book about it made him famous; when he returned to New York thousands lined the streets to welcome him with a ticker-tape parade. In 1936 Robinson built a shipyard at Ipswich, Massachussetts, in Essex County, the birthplace of many of the most famous sailing vessels built in America. The sailing ship that he would create as his personal yacht would be a

5 *Varua* under full sail—"Varua", *said the British naval historian Douglas Phillips-Birt, "is the most highly developed and most beautiful ocean-going sailing vessel of her size ever built."*

As a research vessel, Varua *sails over 30,000 miles a year at both extremes of the humpback whale's migrations, from Hawaii to Alaska and back.*

masterpiece of the boat-builder's art—classical, beautiful, functional and the culminating experience of a lifetime's voyaging. Her hull, refined to perfection, would leave no wake, parting the sea and bringing it back together again astern. She would ride high on a following sea and mock huge swells, rather than inviting them aboard. Capable of record speeds under sail, she would also run safely under bare poles in any weather. Her name, said Robinson, would be *Varua*—Tahitian for "spirit" or "soul"—and would express "the essence of the ethereal beauty of a sailing ship and her eternal quest."

Work on *Varua* began in 1940. The hull was designed by Starling Burgess and the rigging by L. Francis Herreshoff. The Burgess family had designed nearly half of all the America's Cup defenders, including the famous *Ranger*. Herreshoff's masterpiece, the *Ticonderoga*, is to this day the envy of sailors around the world. Unfortunately, the priorities of wartime restricted the materials that Robinson could use. The yellow pine he had stockpiled went to wartime priorities and he had to use Philippine mahogany instead—an expedient that was to show its effects many years later. Work proceeded slowly, but on 12th March 1942 *Varua* was launched and on 7th July 1945 she slipped out of Gloucester, bound for the South Pacific. Thereafter Tahiti was her home base for the next 30 years, during which she sailed over a quarter of a million miles, through impossible latitudes and the most severe storms that weather can produce, from Cape Horn to the South China Sea, often carrying scientific parties for research. After 30 years under sail, *Varua* in the mid-nineteen-seventies was losing the battle that a wooden vessel must continually wage with the tropics. Her decks leaking and her planks rotting, she lay at anchor in Papeete, as beautiful as ever to the eye, but in a sad state of disrepair.

Meanwhile, Russ Nilson had grown up on the same New England coast where *Varua* had been built. Familiar since childhood with ships and the sea, he knew of the legendary brigantine and when a scientific research voyage took him to Tahiti he met with William Robinson and made him a proposal. Nilson was convinced that a sailing vessel would make an ideal platform for single-mission research into the lives of sea mammals, for which purpose silence of maneuver in the water was important, if not essential. Large and fast, *Varua* could still be handled by a minimal crew. Robinson agreed to lease her for one dollar a year for 50 years if Nilson would restore her, maintain her and devote her to education and research.

After close inspection and a nearly disastrous voyage as far as Pago Pago in Samoa, it was clear that *Varua* would have to be completely rebuilt right there, at the farthest point to which Nilson had been able to bring her on his way to dry dock and repair in New Zealand. For more than two years, through disappointment, disease and back-breaking effort, at a cost of $300,000, Nilson stayed on in Samoa, rebuilding the ship, managing the crew and fighting the elements. To pay for the reconstruction of *Varua*, he sold all he possessed, went deeply into debt and, being

6 *Varua* sailing down Molokai Channel (right) Varua's *Herreshoff-designed rig is very powerful, yet can easily be handled by a crew of* three. Here it is seen carrying Varua *down the Molokai Channel at 12 knots.*

himself a structural engineer trained at Cornell, he accepted a contract to build retaining walls along a treacherous road across the mountains from Pago Pago to Afono.

All the original timbers in *Varua* were rotten; most of the steel framework had rusted away. Nilson discovered a stock of New Zealand kauri in Samoa, the wood most preferred by shipwrights for planking a hull. Equally fortunate was a find of edge-grain Samoan kava for the decks. First, new steel was welded into the damaged sheer clamps, deck beams and frames, and new frames were bent to replace those missing at the stern. Then a new stem, forefoot, keelson and transom were made, leaving only the keel and deadwood as original. Next the kauri planks were fastened, using more than 10,000 flathead carriage bolts. Each fastening hole in the wood had to be sealed, filled with epoxy and then capped with a bung that was also made of kauri. The decks were made of the hardwood kava, which was covered with a thick rubbery polysulfide substance that is very hard-wearing and ensures an absolutely watertight surface. This is especially important, because carrying sensitive electronic gear below decks requires that there be absolutely no leakage.

On 1st November 1978, *Varua* was ready for her second launching. A crew of eight men stood by to hold the lines as the marine railway lowered her down to the water. A bottle of champagne was cracked over her bow, and the workers broke into a cheer. It was a thrilling moment to watch that beautiful vessel, after such a tremendous effort, slowly ease her way down the beach towards the sea and a promising new future.

7 Black turnstones *skim the waves.*

Russ Nilson was only 26 years old when he completed the rebuilding of *Varua*, a remarkable achievement, deserving of great pride. He had a deep respect for a fine ship and the growing love that every sailor feels for a vessel that will sail him safely on the seas. Added to that, *Varua* is beautiful—the kind of mistress that can take every spare coin and yet make you feel good about giving it.

On 1st April 1980, after another year of work on the ship's interior in Hawaii, *Varua* lay once more in Papeete Harbor. William A. Robinson walked slowly around the boat, examining her every detail. Meticulously he trod the decks, quietly pronouncing judgment to himself on this detail and that. Nilson watched with a mixture of hope, worry and joy, as the monologue drew on and the owner's keen eye ran over the ship. Of all of Robinson's work, only the masts and the keel timber remained original. Finally, after several hours of suspense, Robinson exclaimed that she was in every way the dream ship that he had launched back in 1942—only far, far better, for she was now made out of the finest wood that a ship could have, set in place with unsurpassable craftsmanship. The one dollar per year lease agreement was waived, and *Varua*'s title was transferred to "Ocean Research Under Sail", the organization that Russ had formed for future operations and that he has since renamed "Intersea Research".

I sailed aboard *Varua* for the course of a summer, working with humpbacks in the placid waters of Southeast

8 Skipper at the masthead (right) *From atop one of* Varua's *lofty masts, skipper Russell Nilson guides her into a tortuous pass. The yard arms* of Varua's *brigantine rig make ideal sighting platforms at 25 and 50 feet, and are an advantage in our work of observation.*

9 Sailing back to Alaska *The voyages from Hawaii to Alaska can be cold and wet, as* Varua *sails through the spring storms of the north Pacific, but once inside the calm, protected Alaskan waters she sails on peacefully again.*

"Her name," said her builder and first master, William A. Robinson, "Varua, Tahitian for spirit or soul, has a poetic ring when pronounced, and seems to express the essence of the ethereal beauty of a sailing ship."

Alaska. During that time, I developed an admiration not only for the pedigree of the ship, but also for Russ Nilson's exceptional skill at working her unobtrusively among the whales. He seemed to be at one with the sea and his ship, and his respect for the whales was a quality that I greatly appreciated. As the summer came to an end Russ and I decided to continue working together, and within a year we were married.

We knew that a ship like *Varua* was perfect for our research objectives, but keeping a square-rigged sailing ship alive and healthy in these latter years of the twentieth century is an enormous challenge. At first we worked only on federally-funded research contracts; when this source of funds evaporated, we sought out another means to keep our ongoing studies viable. We began taking students to sea with us. Their tuition supported our field efforts, but more importantly, their involvement in the research was invaluable. We were exposing people from all walks of life to the mysteries of an endangered species, and they at the grass-roots level back home were able to do more for legislative protection than could be accomplished through scientific publication alone. For nearly a decade now, people have been joining us in our research expeditions, enabling us to continue our longterm effort of gathering basic information about an endangered species.

Every summer we returned to Southeast Alaska to work with humpbacks on their feeding grounds, and many winters we voyaged to the Hawaiian islands, their primary breeding grounds. The round-trip voyages to both extremes of migration kept us sailing as much as 30,000 miles a year. The commute between Hawaii and Alaska invariably took us through bitter arctic storms and over leagues of ferocious seas that were tough on both ship and crew. The need to have one ship for the tropics and another ship for the higher latitudes became increasingly obvious. *Varua* is perhaps the finest vessel ever built for the tropics. We needed her equivalent for Alaska. In 1986 we found such a ship, the research vessel *Acania*, as beautiful and as able under power as *Varua* is under sail. Launched in 1929, *Acania* has the lines and interior of that opulent time. In the 1930s, she was owned by the movie actress Constance Bennett and served as a playground for Hollywood stars and celebrities. The U.S. Coast Guard appropriated her in World War II to serve as a patrol vessel in the tropics, and then Stanford University took her over to support their program of upper atmosphere research. They made the appropriate conversions, and *Acania* was fitted out as a scientific research ship. The Naval Postgraduate School in Monterey operated her as their oceanographic vessel until 1985, by which time they needed a larger one. A better vessel could not have been found to meet our needs, so we bought *Acania* from the U.S. Government and she became the second ship to sail under the Intersea Research flag.

Our goal in working with humpback whales is to gain a thorough understanding of them through the acquisition of baseline data, and to determine the interrelationship of the whale with its environment. Building on knowledge of the biology and ecology of humpback whales is the only

10 Waterfall in Tracy Arm (right) *Sailing up Tracy Arm,* Varua *passes a waterfall cascading down the vertical 3000-foot walls.*

way to ensure their survival. By owning and operating our own vessels, we are able to remain entire seasons in the field and to make behavioral observations through extended periods of time. This greatly lessens the danger of misinterpretation, or of jumping to conclusions based on insufficient evidence. As each season progresses, behaviors change; even with behaviors that do not vary dramatically, interpretations can be wrong if they are not checked and rechecked over and over again. As you read through these pages, you will see how fragile even now is our understanding of whale behavior.

This book is a summary of our own travel and observations over a period of eight years. It does not profess to be a comprehensive history of whales, nor to be a definitive textbook of cetology in general, nor of the humpback whale in particular. The scientific literature of whales is large and growing fast. For some excellent overviews of the humpback, the reader is recommended to the works listed in the bibliography at the end of this volume. Here our purpose is to stimulate the reader's imagination by portraying as vividly as possible, by images and accompanying text, the basic behaviors of this great leviathan.

For a creature that spends nearly two-thirds of its time underwater, that is too big to be put in an aquarium and viewed through glass, that has been hunted nearly to extinction, and that has a low reproduction rate, it becomes exceedingly important, indeed vital, that we are able to interpret what information there is when we have the opportunity to gain access to it. To this end, understanding what you are observing when you observe it is the first priority. Our hope is that through such an understanding we shall all gain a greater awareness and a better appreciation of this animal, one of the most majestic on earth, the humpback whale.

SOUTHEAST ALASKA RESEARCH AREA

Southeast Alaska is a land of excitement and superlatives. Its majestic scenery, abundant wild-life, and relative inaccessibility make it truly one of the last frontiers on earth. Its lands and waters are unspoiled and rich in resources. Although we don't depend entirely upon these wild resources for our food, an enjoyable part of the Alaskan experience is collecting berries, fishing for salmon, halibut, and trout, and setting the crab pots for the evening meal.

The largest known feeding aggregation of humpback whales in the North Pacific occurs in Southeast Alaska, with a wide distribution throughout Chatham Strait, Frederick Sound and Stephens Passage. Each of our research expeditions circumnavigates Admiralty Island via these areas, with the daily itinerary varying according to whale distribution and weather. Typically, on each voyage we visit the following anchorages.

Tracy Arm is a Yosemite-like glaciated valley with spectacular 3000-foot vertical walls. The Sawyer glaciers, at its furthest reach, frequently calve with thunderous roars that reverberate through-out the fjord. Mountain goats can be seen on the sheer cliffs, and harbor seals haul out on floating icebergs, which they use as pupping grounds. Horned and tufted puffins dive amongst the floes. Gulls and terns swirl overhead. We anchor half-way up the 21-mile fjord in what we have named "the world's most spectacular anchorage". Need-less to say, this fjord is a favorite place for photog-raphy.

Windham Bay has a narrow entrance that opens into the secluded bay. Salmon spawn in the Win-dham and Chuck rivers, which empty into the bay. There is excellent fishing for both salmon and trout. Past abandoned gold mines and beautiful waterfalls, we sometimes hike along these rivers into the rugged interior, which is the domain of bears and eagles.

Brothers Islands are our picnic spot. The islands provide serene anchorage. They are situated far enough off Admiralty Island to be a good area for exploration ashore without a concern for bears. In our walks around the islands we spend time ex-amining the diverse flora and fauna, and visiting the large Steller sea lion colony.

Warm Springs Bay has natural hot springs with

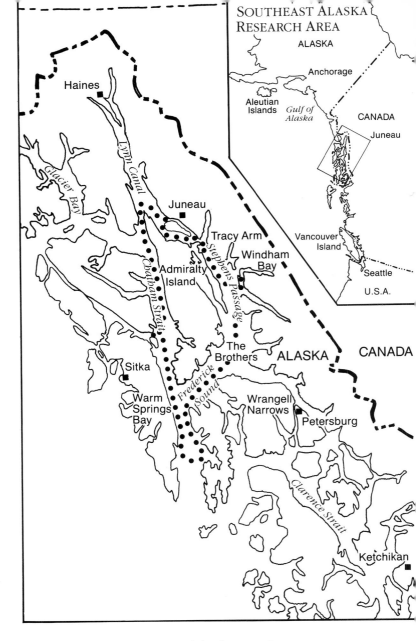

good berry-picking around the bay, and a spectac-ular trail that leads to a mountain lake surrounded by muskeg and high snow-capped peaks.

Murder Cove has a big salmon run and lots of bald eagles, brown bears, and crabs in the shallow waters. Outside the cove is a strong upwelling area where we have observed unique feeding behavior of humpback whales. We often spend long hours with the whales and then anchor in the cove. There we observe the wildlife around us as we feast on dungeness crab.

We operate our vessels in areas that are off the beaten track. An occasional fishing boat may pass or a cruise ship may steam by at 20 knots in the distance, but for the most part we work undis-turbed, in perfect isolation amid this great majes-tic land.

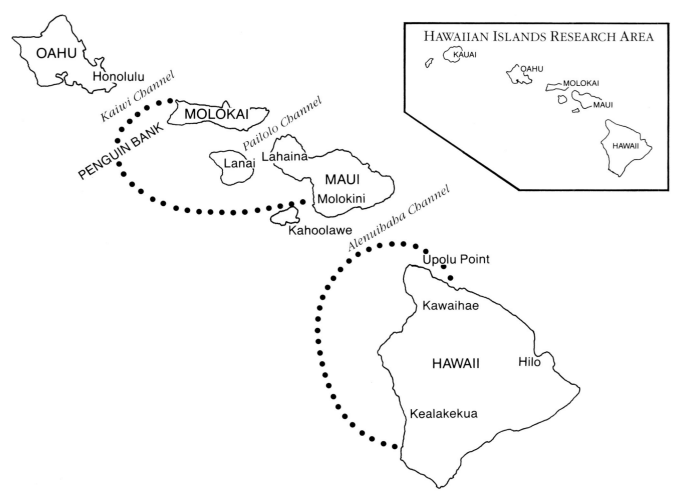

HAWAIIAN ISLANDS RESEARCH AREA

Here in the Hawaiian Archipelago the largest breeding aggregation of humpback whales in the North Pacific winters, crooning to one another and bearing their young. This spectacular combination of whales, along with the warm climate, tropical waters, and gentle winds, makes Hawaii an ideal location for conducting whale research under sail. *Varua*, with her spacious, open decks, graceful white hull and brigantine rig, is perfect for the quiet observational type of research we conduct. A typical expedition takes us into rarely visited bays and anchorages, and out to the offshore regions. There we find whales, dolphins and a great variety of seabirds, including shearwaters, tropic birds and albatross. Walks ashore provide an opportunity to explore the diverse terrain of rugged cliffs and waterfalls, where we can wander among thousands of plant species, including jacaranda, orange trumpet vines, red poinsettias, fishtail ferns, orchids and mangoes.

Early in the season (December through mid-February), we focus our research along the lee shore between Kawaihae Harbor on the Kona coast of the Big Island off Hawaii and Kealakekua (Cook's Bay), where Captain Cook met his death in 1779. Humpback whales are numerous along this coast, often breaching, splashing and cavorting around us as we passively record their songs and take identification photographs.

Later in the season (mid-February through May), we work for the most part between the islands of Maui, Molokai, and Lanai, occasionally venturing to Penguin Bank or Molokini, the partially sunken volcano that forms a crescentic bay of outstanding beauty. Our anchorages are typically in seldom-visited, unspoiled areas where we can take time out to dive and snorkel among the tropical fish and coral reefs, and explore the extensive, sandy beaches.

11 Calving icebergs *Huge icebergs calve off the faces of the flowing rivers of ice. They can swamp a small boat, the pilot book reporting waves up to 25 feet as a result of such calvings.*

12 Parting glacial ice Acania *parts the ice as she sails towards Sawyer Glacier, seen in the distance. Ice is a constant menace in northern waters and keeps the bow watch alert as we navigate through the fjords. However, because her engines are quiet, and because her well-designed hull creates a minimal wake,* Acania *does little or nothing in the narrow fjords to disturb the ice on which the harbor seal pups haul out.*

13 Whales blowing *Whales blowing while* Acania *and* Varua *stand off in the distance.*

14 Working with cooperative pod Acania *seen working with a cooperative feeding pod in Chatham Strait.*

15 Sounding *A whale, with almost totally black pigmentation and almost no scarring, sounds as it swims towards* Acania.

16 Humbpack breaching *The great pectoral fins look like waving arms. For a full succession of breaching behavior see plates 66–79.*

17 Off North Sawyer Glacier (overleaf) *Acania was launched in 1929, as one of the most elegant vessels of that era, for a wealthy Wall Street banker. She was later owned by Constance Bennett, star of the silent screen, and during World War II was appropriated by the U.S. Government. Stanford outfitted her for research and the Naval Postgraduate School at Monterey completed the conversion. Intersea Research bought her in 1986 to continue the long-term studies in the North Pacific, so enabling* Varua *to return to tropical waters. Although both the two ships have worked extensively in the tropics and in the polar regions, they are each best suited to their new tours of duty. The physical oceanographic capabilities of* Acania, *when combined with her comfortable quarters, make her the ideal vessel for our work in Alaska. Here she is beneath North Sawyer Glacier in Tracy Arm.*

MYSTICETE WHALES
A GENERAL INTRODUCTION by Delphine Haley

It is difficult to believe that the whales, so perfectly adapted to the marine environment, are mammals like us, and that in remotely distant ages their ancestors actually lived on land. Although very little is known of their origin, cetaceans—the whales, dolphins and porpoises of the order Cetacea—are most closely related to present-day hoofed mammals. According to one theory, their common ancestor was a wolf-sized carnivorous mammal, that occasionally hunted fish along the inshore waters some 60 million years ago. The enormous evolutionary transition of these early forms from shore to sea is scarcely known to us, an almost unimaginable metamorphosis hidden in the depths of the past, yet when we look at the end result of this evolution one thing is clear—the two large groups of whales and dolphins now living, including some 76 cetacean species, are the outcome of the most profound anatomical changes to have occurred in the evolution of any mammals. Ranging in size from the small five-foot La Plata dolphin to the 100-foot blue whale—the largest animal that has ever lived—cetaceans today are found in all the world's open seas and along many shores, a few even living in rivers and

18 *Varua* entering Tracy Arm (left) *(photo by Frans Lanting).*

19 Adult humpback at surface *An adult humpback reaches a length of between 45 and 52 feet and weighs up to a ton per foot. As adults, females average five feet longer than males. They are one of the rarest of the cosmopolitan whales, second only to the Greenland right whale and perhaps the bowhead whale.*

20 & 21 Paired blowholes *Mysticete whales have paired blowholes, whereas odontocete (toothed whales) have a single blowhole. Here the v-shaped blow typical of mysticetes can be seen. The blowholes are opened upon surfacing for breath and then are immediately closed. Here the two blowholes are clearly visible.*

freshwater lakes. Like us, the cetaceans are mammals—that is to say they are highly intelligent, warm-blooded, air-breathing creatures, with hair or vestiges of it, and they nourish their young from the milk of their mammary glands.

The oldest known fossils of cetaceans date back about 45 million years. These early whales, called archeocetes, had nostrils part way back on the head; some of them were small and dolphinlike, others were up to 50 feet long and serpent-shaped. The archeocetes survived until about 25 million years ago, when the only remaining line gave rise to the evolutionary ancestors of our modern whales. These are divided into two major groups: the baleen whales (suborder Mysticeti) and the toothed whales (suborder Odontoceti).

During those early epochs, the cetacean body was evolving for mastery of the seas. Freed in the water from the restrictions of gravity, it grew much larger, longer and more streamlined. The nasal opening gradually shifted to the top of the head, for easier breathing at the ocean surface. The whole outer form was smoothed into an envelope of blubber, to retain body heat and store energy, thus eliminating the need for a hairy coat. The ears were eliminated, except for small holes in the head; the nipples and sex organs were withdrawn into slits within the body; the sebaceous and sweat glands disappeared, because they were no longer necessary. The limbs became rigid, with the forelimbs changed into flippers for steering and stability, and the hind limbs replaced by a large, heavy tail with horizontally flattened flukes. The flukes, powered by the massive muscles of the lumbar region, move upward and downward, forcing the water backwards, and making the cetaceans among the swiftest and most powerful travellers in the seas.

Despite these many anatomical modifications, some traces of the whale's ancient terrestrial ties remain. The flippers are composed of arm, wrist and finger bones, with five fingers for most whale species. Some whale embryos possess tiny flaps reminiscent of hind legs, and, in rare instances, other small bones thought to be vestiges of leg bones. A pair of bones is also found embedded in the muscles at the hip area; they are all that remains of the pelvic girdle. Also as a reminder of the evolutionary past, hairs persist around the snouts of fetal toothed whales and adult baleen whales.

Modern cetaceans are of two distinctly different types. The toothed whales (suborder Odontoceti) are by far the larger group. This group is comprised of 65 species of dolphins, beaked whales, sperm whales, pilot whales and arctic whales, including that "unicorn" of the north, the betusked narwhal. All these are distinguished by a single blow hole, and varying numbers of conical teeth, used for seizing prey. The ten baleen or mysticete whales are recognized by a huge lower jaw, which makes the mouth line seem to lie toward the top of the head, by double blowholes and, most distinctive, by baleen or whalebone instead of teeth. The baleen consists of horny plates that hang from the whale's upper jaw and are fringed on their inner margins with fine or coarse hairlike fibers—hence the group name Mysticete, meaning "moustached". The

22 A vertical lunge feed *is the most dramatic feeding maneuver that a whale uses, yet there are many different methods, depending on the prey species, current conditions, depth of prey and other environmental and social concerns. Here a whale emerges in a vertical position, invariably used on fast swimming fish such as herring.*

purpose of the curtain of fringed plates is to filter the whale's food. When feeding, the baleen whale scoops up tremendous amounts of water along with the zooplankton or small fish that constitute its diet. It then strains the water through the baleen and out of the mouth, retaining the food. Paradoxically, the largest animals ever to inhabit the earth prey predominantly on some of the sea's tiniest creatures. The mysticete group includes the longest, fastest and heaviest of the cetaceans.

To capture their prey, both the toothed and baleen whales are equipped for diving. The depths that they favor depend upon the prey pursued. Because the tiny shrimp and small food organisms consumed by many of the baleen whales are located in the upper water layers, these whales usually dive to less than 160 feet; some, however, have been known to dive to 1,150 feet. The toothed whales are the deepest divers, with records being held by the sperm whale, which descends regularly to 1,500 feet, has been found entangled in cables at 3,720 feet, and may in fact be able to dive as deep as 10,000 feet. During the dive, the whale is aided by an ability to replace eighty to ninety percent of the air in its lungs, and to decrease its heart rate and conserve blood and oxygen for only the most vital organs—the heart and brain. In addition, because the whale does not breathe underwater, it is free from nitrogen buildup in the blood, and does not suffer from the "bends" when it returns to the surface.

Many aspects of the lives of the whales and dolphins—particularly their social behaviors in the wild—still remain a mystery to those who study them. Dolphin species

23 Baleen plates *The humpback is a mysticete, which means "moustached" in Latin, in allusion to the fringing baleen plates in the roof of the mouth. Rather than teeth, the mysticetes have a row of between 260 and 400 of these keratinaceous plates on either side of the palate.*

usually mate in spring and summer, whereas the highly migratory baleen whales mate and calve during winter. Gestation extends ten to fourteen months for the baleen whales, and ten to sixteen months for the toothed whales, with the interval between breeding being most commonly every two or three years. A single calf is born, usually tail first. The birth occurs underwater, and the calf either swims to the surface or is pushed up by its mother or another whale. The young whale grows quickly while nursing on its mother's fat-rich milk. An extreme example of this is the blue whale, largest of all whales, which as a newborn weighs over two tons and doubles its weight within the first week. In seven months, it is 50 feet long and weighs 25 tons.

Great size, however, does not always guarantee longevity for the whales. They have few natural enemies, except for killer whales which are known to attack and kill their own kin—particularly the dolphins, minke whales and gray whales—although this predation is insignificant when compared to that of man. Man, with his harpoon gun, has been by far the whale's principal enemy, and commercial whaling for oil, meat and baleen has profoundly diminished the numbers of whales we have left in the world. The high numbers killed over many years have been a loss compounded by the whale's slow reproductive rate, placing some species—such as the right whale, the humpback and the bowhead—on the verge of extinction. Only in recent years, with the conservation efforts of the International Whaling Commission, and the United States Marine Mammal Protection Act of 1972, has

24 Baleen plates *There is a great deal of color variation in the plates, ranging from black to very light brown. The baleen plates serve as a most effective means of straining small organisms and fish from the water, which is expelled between the plates when the mouth is closed.*

25 (left) & 26 Ventral pleats *The humpback belongs to the rorqual family. Among the rorqual characteristics are the accordion-like throat grooves or ventral pleats. When the whale is feeding these pleats are distended by the engulfed water which contains the prey. The water is then forced out between the baleen plates by the tongue, and the prey is consumed. North Pacific humpbacks have between 12 and 26 pleats.*

man changed from predator to protector in his relationship to the whales.

If the whale manages to elude the boats of those few countries and native groups still whaling, it can expect to live a relatively long life. Dolphins live into their thirties, and the great whales may live as long as man. By counting growth layers in the teeth of toothed whales and on the earplugs of baleen whales, researchers have determined that killer whales can live to age 50 or more and gray, fin, humpback, sei, Brydes and sperm whales into their 70s. There are even records of a blue whale surviving to age 110 and a fin whale to age 114.

Although our mammalian status links us to the whales and dolphins biologically, we are still separated from them by the marine environment to which they are so well adapted. Thus many aspects of their lives in the wild are still unknown, due to the enormous difficulties involved in this kind of field research. For many decades, biologists have had to settle for observing whales at the ocean's surface or studying the remains of animals that have stranded or been killed. Now, thanks to advances in technology, scientists are able to radio-tag whales, to track their movements, and to photograph them and even identify individuals by markings on their flukes or fins. As the body of knowledge about these fascinating creatures accumulates, we increasingly come to appreciate their unique adaptations and abilities.

In the pages that follow, you will become acquainted with one of the most intriguing of the great baleen whales now being studied by researchers—the humpback whale,

Megaptera novaeangliae. Found in all oceans of the world, this 50-foot leviathan is distinguished from other whales by its long sweeping flippers (the Latin name *Megaptera* means "big-winged") and by its frequent habit of breaching or leaping out of the water, by its sophisticated feeding techniques and by its hauntingly beautiful songs. Other anatomical peculiarities include wartlike, round protuberances on the snout, each containing a hair or hair sac, and the knobs of flesh on the leading edges of the long flippers.

As a baleen whale, the humpback spends the summer in cold, fertile waters, where it feeds on small shrimplike crustaceans or fishes. In winter it migrates to warmer waters, where every other year the mature female calves. The newborn calf, some 16 feet in length, weighs about two tons at birth. Protected by its mother, it nurses for 11 months and accompanies her to the summer feeding grounds. It is on the feeding grounds that one sees the humpback's versatile feeding strategies. These include the use of vocalizations and bubble nets to disorient its prey, and elaborate movements of the pectoral fins and flukes to concentrate the tiny food organisms.

On the winter calving grounds, in warmer climes, the male humpback sings. Its song, eerie and haunting to human ears, ranges from glissandos of high squeaks to low croaks and creaky door-hinge sounds. Basically, the song consists of a long series of phrases repeated in sequence over more than half an hour at a time. Each stock or geographical group of humpbacks has its own dialect, and its songs vary slightly from year to year but can be

27 Barnacles *Humpbacks are host to a number of different parasites. Here stalked barnacles* (Conchoderma auritum) *can be seen growing on acorn barnacles* (Coronula diadema) *from the ventral pleats. Whale lice* (Cyamus boopis) *also make their home on the skin of the whale.*

28 Pectoral fin (right) *The unique characteristics of the humpback make it unlikely that they will be confused with any other species. Humpbacks have the largest pectoral fins of any whale; they are about one third of the body length. Because the humpback is a relatively slow swimmer, the flipper length may be important for maneuvering. The exceptional length may also be for thermoregulation, since the humpback inhabits both polar and tropical seas.*

identified within the group over several years. The exact reason for the male's song is unknown, but researchers believe that it may advertise a willingness to mate, perhaps attracting females and/or keeping other males away.

From an estimated population of 120,000 before commercial whaling began, there are only about 10,000 humpback whales left in the world today. It is now the second rarest of the great whales having worldwide distribution—second only to the right whale. Hopefully, as researchers learn more about this gentle and graceful cetacean, they will continue to ensure its protection for a safe and healthy future.

29 Tail span *The tail reaches a span of 15 feet in adult humpbacks, and is distinguished by the scalloping on the trailing edge.*

30 Sensory nodules   *The sensory nodules on the rostrum are unique to the humpback. Each one contains a single hair follicle about an inch long, the last vestige of mammalian hair. The function of the nodules is not entirely understood, but the sensitivity may aid in different environmental monitorings such as prey detection.*

31 & 32 Arching the back *The humpback acquired its name by the way it arches its back prior to a dive. After arching high for a deep dive, the whale lifts the flukes into the air as it sounds. At this moment, from a position behind the whale, the distinct pigmentation patterns of the whale can be observed. These patterns of white and black tell the tale of that particular whale over the years.*

33 Tail flukes *A humpback throws its flukes during a dive. Though subtleties appear throughout the different stages, such as the manner in which the whale holds its tail, the ultimate identification is in the pigmentation patterns revealed before the final descent.*

34 Cooperative lunge feeding pod *In Southeast Alaska, Intersea Research has been investigating the social dynamics of cooperative lunge feeding whales, and was the first to document this* *remarkable behavior. Here the preeminent leaders of a group rise in a vertical lunge while the following whales merge in a lateral position behind.*

35 Cooperative feeding pod *Humpbacks are highly versatile feeders and use different strategies to obtain their prey. As a member of the family* Balaenopteridae, *they are among those whales that gulp their food. After four months devoted almost exclusively to feeding in the prolific waters of Alaska, humpbacks begin their long migration back to Hawaii or Mexico.*

MIGRATION

Twice each year, humpback whales undertake one of the longest migrations of any mammal. Nearly a third of their lives will be spent plying the waters of the Pacific, between the Alaskan or Antarctic feeding grounds and the sub-tropical calving areas. The cold productive waters of the higher latitudes enable the humpbacks to consume sufficient prey to meet their immense caloric needs, while the warm, protected waters of the tropics are required for calving. As they migrate, over 5,000 miles each year, they are guided by finely tuned sensory systems across vast empty expanses of the Pacific, to find isolated waters for breeding, or through labyrinthine fjords, islands, shoals and swift tidal currents to their feeding grounds. After the southern migratory journeys, the social behavior of humpbacks alters dramatically when they arrive at their destinations. The peaceful, often cooperative, feeding activities give way to competitive and violent confrontations between the males, as they battle for access to mates on the winter grounds.

Along the west coast of North America, summering groups of humpbacks are distributed from the Chuckchi

36 Setting out on migration *Nearly a third of the northeast Pacific humpback's life will be spent plying the water between Alaskan feeding grounds and the sub-tropical calving grounds.*

How they are able to navigate remains a mystery, but among the theories is that deposits of iron in their brains may allow them to detect variations in the earth's magnetic field.

Sea to southern California. However, the large majority of
these whales congregate in five isolated feeding herds,
located at the Alaskan Peninsula, Prince William Sound,
Southeast Alaska, Vancouver Island, and the Farallon
Islands. The winter mating and calving grounds are
confined to the Hawaiian Islands and the west coast of
Mexico, from southern Baja California to Jalisco, including
the Islas de Revillagigedo and the Islas Tres Marias.
Sequential photographs of natural markings on the tail
flukes have revealed a pattern of migratory movement
between the seasonal habitats. Resighting of individuals has
demonstrated that most humpbacks faithfully return to the
same feeding regions each summer, and remain there for
the season. Most return to the same annual calving grounds
each winter as well. However, during the migration south
to reconvene on the Mexican or Hawaiian mating and
calving grounds, some intermingling of these isolated
groups occurs. On several occasions, humpbacks that
wintered one year in Hawaii were the next year identified
in Mexico. Although such exchanges are uncommon, these
observations have altered some of the theories surrounding
humpback migration. Readily seen in their coastal breeding
and feeding areas, the Hawaiian humpbacks are rarely
observed on their migrations, and therefore the oceanic
corridors that these leviathans travel remain to us very
largely a mystery.

Another obscure and unexplained detail of humpback
distribution has to do with the size and structure of a small
remnant population that inhabits the Asian side of the
Pacific, around Taiwan and the Bonin, Ryukyu and Mariana

Islands. Marking returns of this small group, thought to total only about 100 animals, indicate that some of them visit the eastern Aleutian Islands in summer.

In the Southern Hemisphere, humpback whales summer in the cold prolific waters of the Antarctic, where they feed almost 24 hours per day. During this time, they gain the reserve fat that sustains them for the rest of the year. Like the North Pacific population they feed rarely, if at all, during the winter months. Humpbacks from the Antarctic population divide into five groups when they return to tropical waters to breed and calve. One group goes to Australia, another to Fiji, and the others to Tonga, Samoa, and the Cook Islands, which is their most easterly limit. How many whales there are at each of these island groups is unknown, and little is known of their social dynamics. It may very well be that each year the same individuals return to the same island groups. By means of individual identification programs this could be verified, through comparison of the same animals during consecutive years. In the early management of fisheries, individual whales were identified by firing a tag into the whale, one that bore information such as the date and location of the tagging. Later, when the whale was killed, the tag was retrieved, and a great deal was learned in this way about migratory patterns. The failing of this method was, of course, that the subject of study was approaching extinction as quickly as the pool of knowledge grew. In 1976 Steve Katona and others, working with Atlantic humpback whales, found that the pigmentation patterns on the ventral surface or underside of tail flukes were as unique to individual whales as thumbprints are to humans. By photographing the tail flukes, individual whales could be identified. This method has vast advantages over tag implantation, for not only is it harmless to the animal, but it makes possible a much more definitive compilation of information from birth until after death. We shall refer to this in more detail later with reference to photo-identification.

To start their migratory departures, humpbacks may rely on environmental cues, such as day length, water temperatures and lunar cycles. One theory is that, once embarked on their immense journeys, humpbacks may gaze at the night sky to navigate celestially. Spyhopping in coastal areas may also allow whales to orient themselves, by peering at topographical features such as mountains or sea cliffs. One of the most remarkable features of many migratory animals is an ability to guide themselves by some sort of sophisticated "sixth sense". In the case of whales, researchers have speculated that this sixth sense may be related to deposits of iron in the frontal lobes of the brain; these deposits would act like magnets, and allow the whale to detect the earth's magnetic field. With this system, humpbacks may also be able to read the magnetic pattern that became locked into the ocean's crust as the sea-bed was formed. Thus, cruising along the surface, humpbacks may be able to follow the magnetic gridwork of the sea bottom thousands of feet below, like a giant navigational chart. This sensitivity to magnetism has also been hypothesized as one factor contributing to the mass strandings of marine mammals. Magnetic storms caused by bursts of solar activity seem to disorient the navigational systems of whales, causing them to go astray. In addition, particular beaches where cetaceans habitually strand have been shown to harbor local magnetic anomalies, which may disorient cetaceans.

While on the Alaskan feeding grounds, humpbacks feed day and night, consuming between half a ton and a ton every day. After they leave these grounds, and begin their long voyage south, they will not feed again until they return eight months later. Migratory dates are variable, although most whales begin departing Alaska in late September and arrive on their breeding grounds in December, after averaging about three miles per hour, day and night, on the three-month voyage.

During the latter part of September 1987, we observed a large aggregation of mothers with calves in the Frederick Sound area. Our aerial surveys revealed that most whales had departed the Frederick Sound-Stephens Passage area by that time, and that only this group remained. Such an observation would indicate that cow and calf pairs tend to stay behind longer than the rest of the humpback population.

Small groups of humpbacks routinely linger in the cold Alaskan waters until the end of December, and then become scarce after the beginning of the new year. It is not known if the few individuals found between December and March are overwintering, or are actually autumn stragglers or early spring migrants.

During migration there is temporary segregation within the herd, according to age, sex and reproductive states. Once on the calving grounds, the whales remain to mate or calve for several months, before they begin their migration north again in March and April, arriving on the Alaskan feeding grounds at the beginning of summer.

Newly pregnant females are the first to leave the calving grounds. These are followed by mature males, and females in early lactation. Pregnant females are also the last to leave the summer grounds, thus maximizing the time spent feeding in preparation for the demands of pregnancy, nursing, and the long interval of fasting.

BREEDING BEHAVIOR

From out of the dark blue depths of the Pailolo Channel in Hawaii, a haunting song begins to ebb and flow. Rising in intensity, the melodic sound slips through the hull of *Varua*, and into the dreams of her occupants as she rocks gently at anchor.

The long and varied song of the humpback is one of the most complex vocalizations in the animal world. On the winter grounds it seems to be delivered only by lone males, and probably serves a number of functions in the reproductive behavior of humpbacks, to synchronize mating, attract females, or advertise the amorous intentions and individual fitness of males. Another possible function may be to act as a spacing mechanism, to help eliminate conflicts between bulls.

One of the most interesting features of the winter song is the metamorphosis that it undergoes by incorporating new and eliminating old themes. All singers within a population adopt these changes, so that the same version of the song is being broadcast by all the males. It takes about eight years before the entire song is changed. What is most perplexing is how the humpback songs on both the

Hawaiian and Mexican wintering grounds undergo identical changes, despite being separated by 2,000 miles. One theory for this synchronous evolution is that some of the singers may fraternize on both the calving grounds during the one winter season. Another theory, though perhaps a bit far fetched, is that the continuity of the song may be maintained by a 2,000-mile cavalcade of singers that spans the distance from Hawaii to Mexico.

Social relationships between humpbacks on the feeding grounds differ dramatically from those of the wintering grounds. The armistice that holds during feeding slowly dissolves as the males return to breed. In the warm tropical waters of Hawaii and Mexico, the new social order now centers around adversary relationships between amorous males, who try to associate with numerous females over the course of the mating season. A basic pod formation is adopted on the wintering grounds, a triad consisting of a mother, her year-old calf, and a male escort. The bull maintains the rear guard of this trio, and will vigorously defend this position from the intrusion of any other males. Should another male approach the pod, the escort will use a variety of defensive tactics to discourage the intruder. These include emitting a screen of disorienting bubbles, and using his body like a blockade to deny the interloper access to the female. A male may even attempt to hinder an adversary's access to the surface, or obstruct his blow hole. If the intruder is still not daunted, the combat may lead to an exchange of strikes. Head butts will be delivered in which one whale charges, ramming the adversary with his massive jaw. Perhaps the most effective

37   Bleeding nodules of a bull in conflict   *In the warm tropical waters of Mexico and Hawaii, males compete for access to females. The songs which are sung by solitary males may advertise their amorous intentions, or perhaps work as a spacing mechanism to help eliminate conflict among bulls. However the "gentle giants" often become violent in their aggressive pursuits. This whale has his ventral pleats puffed slightly, perhaps to appear more intimidating, and the sensory nodules are bleeding from the head butts of another whale charging in competition for the same female.*

weapons are the tail flukes, which are extraordinarily powerful. The sharp barnacles that encrust the rostrum, fluke tips, and pectoral fins, add destructive power to these armaments. The contestants are seldom seriously injured, although raw sensory nodules and bloody dorsal fins do confirm that these conflicts are more than just ritualized jousting. The scuffle usually ends abruptly, as one of the combatants retreats into the blue waters again, to seek out an unattached female.

Although copulation has rarely been observed in humpbacks, it is likely that the process is very similar to that of other large whale species, in a belly-to-belly position. In most cases, more than two whales are present. Generally one other, but sometimes as many as five whales, will appear to assist the couple, supposedly acting as their support crew. Some researchers maintain that this may indicate competition rather than support.

Female humpbacks give birth generally every two to three years, in a cycle that is closely linked to their migratory journeys. As soon as they are impregnated, the cows begin their return migration to the Alaskan feeding grounds, being the first whales to do so. Gestation then lasts about one year, with birth following on the winter return to the tropics. The gravid mother seeks out a protected and secluded bay. The pale newborn weighs about two tons, is born tail first, and for several days is wrinkled with fetal folds. The mother and calf remain largely isolated from the rest of the wintering herd, allowing a strong bond to grow between them without interference. A proficient swimmer from the moment it takes its first breath, the precocious calf often swims alongside its mother, catching a ride in the eddy she creates. By the time the calf is strong enough to make the trip north, many of the adults will have already departed from the wintering grounds. The mother and calf are the last to leave the winter calving grounds.

Upon reaching the feeding grounds, the calf slowly learns to forage in a fashion similar to its mother. The calf's fidelity to a particular feeding ground is most likely established on the first trip north with its mother, and as a grown whale it will probably journey back to that same location each spring for the rest of its life.

After traveling 5,000 miles, and raising a 15-ton calf without eating, the mother is presumably eager to wean her offspring when she arrives on the feeding grounds. This comes about quickly, the calves adopting the foraging patterns of the adults; their krill-laden scat indicates that independent feeding has commenced. Although we have never observed suckling by calves on the feeding grounds, mothers are known to continue lactating throughout the summer, and calves arriving back in Hawaii have been found to contain lactose in their stomachs. This suggests that nursing may occur intermittently on the feeding grounds, or it may be resumed on the southward migration. Calves are thus not weaned entirely until they are about one year old.

38 Mother and calf (overleaf) *(photo by Deborah Glockner-Ferrari/ Center for Whale Studies).*

39 Mother and calf   *The gestation period for a humpback calf is about one year. The calf is born tail first and weighs about two tons. It quickly learns to adapt to the marine environment, although it may be assisted by its mother in the first breaths by being lifted to the surface on her pectoral fins or back. In this photograph, a young calf watches a remora swim by as the calf remains within the protective reach of the mother (photo by Kenneth C. Balcomb III).*

40 Mother and calf (right) *Humpback calves, like all other young mammals, nurse from their mothers. The calf consumes about 120 gallons of milk each day in three gallon servings. The milk is about the consistency of condensed milk, and is squirted into the calf's mouth in just a few seconds at a time, with each nursing session.*

The young calf stays close to its protective mother. By the time they reach Alaska, the calves have become much more adventurous, sometimes straying several miles from their mothers. The mottled coloring on these whales comes from the light penetrating the water (photo by Deborah Glockner-Ferrari/Center for Whale Studies).

41 Breaching calf *A young calf, only several months old, is already adept at breaching. This friskiness promotes coordination and musculature development.*

42 Calf with kelp *A calf is often very playful. When the calf comes in contact with a patch of kelp it frequently begins rolling in it, lifting it with the snout, flippers or flukes as if it were a toy. Probably the tactile stimulation is a pleasing sensation.*

43 Twin calves *Here two calves were seen with one mother. Their exceptionally small size reinforced our belief that they were twins, a rarity among humpbacks. One of the calves tries a breach while lunge feeding.*

PHOTO-IDENTIFICATION

Photo-identification is a process of recording on film the markings that naturally occur on a whale's body and that are unique to each animal.

All such photographs taken in the North Pacific are entered into a fluke identification catalogue at the National Marine Mammal Laboratory in Seattle, Washington. This pool of photographs has revealed that the current North Pacific population of humpbacks numbers around 1,500 animals. For us, one of the most important advantages of photo-identification is the opportunity that it provides to recognize whales as individuals. This is how we are able to gain insight into the group formations, personalities and subtle behaviors of the humpback whale. Equipped with telephoto lenses, high-speed film, and computerized database programs, we are greatly extending our powers of observation to probe deep into the lives of cetaceans.

The most important characteristics used to identify individual whales include the pigmentation of the skin, the shape of the flukes and dorsal fin, the arrangement of nicks and scratches and, though transitory, the patterns of organisms such as barnacles or lice. The humpback is one of the most accommodating whale species for photo-identification, thanks to the distinctively pigmented undersides of its flukes. At birth, the ventral surfaces or undersides of the flukes are milky white, but within the first year a unique pigmentation pattern begins to solidify, and the whale develops "fingerprints". Additional diagnostic markings on the surface of the flukes come from barnacles, Pacific lamprey scars, and rakings from the teeth of killer whales.

When a humpback dives, the peduncle and tail are arched high into the air, exposing the unique pigmentation patterns. On the feeding grounds adults almost always throw their flukes before sounding, whereas calves tend not to lift their flukes until late June or early July. The onset of fluking behavior is attributed to an increase in the calf's buoyant blubber layer, and possibly to its growing sophistication in capturing prey at deeper depths. The flukes, composed of cartilage and connective tissue, may span nearly 15 feet. In the humpback, an irregular scalloping along the trailing edge of the fluke is an individual identification feature, found in no other whale. The dorsal fins are also distinctive, and are useful for monitoring the movement and position of whales during behavioral studies.

Despite the distinctiveness of the humpback's flukes, the incredible potential of photo-identification was not realized until the mid-1970s, when Steve Katona on the East Coast and Charles Jurasz on the West Coast began to develop techniques for identifying humpback individuals. Before this, little had been done. Fluke coloration was

44 White tail with hourglass pattern *This white-tailed whale could be easily confused with another whale with all-white markings, until the delicate patterns are analyzed. The hourglass pattern on this whale is distinctive and has been photographed over the past eight years in Chatham Strait.*

45 Contrasted pigmentation *Two contrasting patterns of pigmentation.*

never noted during the whaling era, probably due to the
whaler's habit of removing the flukes at sea to make the
carcass more manageable. Historically, the migratory
movements of the fastest great whales were monitored by
shooting a metal tag about 10 inches long into the back
muscles of a whale, but subsequent information was
dependent upon the whale's capture and processing in a
whaling operation. Photo-identification, by contrast, is
valuable because information can be acquired without
killing the subject of study. It has given us a much better
understanding of the migratory movements between the
large wintering populations and the smaller feeding herds.
Keeping track of individuals from year to year reveals the
degree of fidelity that those individuals have to a given
feeding or winter area, and also reveals their associations

with other whales. Another significant use of photo-identification has been in determining the calving intervals of individual whales. Other cetacean mysteries, such as longevity and population size, are also being unravelled through the use of photo-identification.

The difficulty we have encountered with individual fluke identification is not the acquisition of the information but the cataloguing of the data. We have realized that a data retrieval system is necessary for processing the quantity of detailed behavioral notes we are making on individuals. Because the organism we are studying cannot be manipulated as in a laboratory study, the only way to study the humpback scientifically is to collect a very large pool of non-subjective observational data, and then look for correlations within that data. A computer is the tool required to manage the large amounts of data that we generate in the field over our long time at sea. Additionally we have found that the video camera is a highly efficient means of collecting data. Flukes can be frozen on the screen for the purpose of comparison, and behaviors such as cooperative feeding can be played back repeatedly for detailed analysis. Video allows for a very rapid collection of data and the computer enables us to search for correlations rather than having to search manually.

Jeff Reynolds, a molecular biologist at U.C. Berkeley, and the son of *Acania's* former captain of 30 years Woody Reynolds, joined our research effort and accepted the challenge of developing a program to meet our needs. The system developed enables us to describe a fluke pigmentation pattern by using eleven simple classification categories. With video, the image is digitized and displayed on the screen, to be classified into these categories. The computer can then search the data base for existing fluke ID's to see if that whale has been sighted before. The search can be broadened by turning off various categories until it is determined whether this is a new whale or one which has previously been catalogued. Through the use of a split screen, the retrieved fluke can be compared with the present fluke in question. Detailed observational notes, video pictures, and digitized sounds, are then included in the file of that specific whale. This enables us to determine very quickly when and where a whale was last sighted (over hours, days or years), what whales it was associated with, and in what behaviors it was engaged. We can then make comparisons for feeding-site fidelity, and search for correlations between specific feeding behaviors and times of the day. For instance, we can look for all whales sighted at Five Finger Island over a period of years, then select all whales from this subset that were sighted between 0900 hours and 1000. We can then further select for all whales that were lunge feeding during that time. Using this system, patterns of behavior can be looked for in very large amounts of data that Intersea Research can collect during our extended time in the field.

The other advantage of the computerized system is that our hydrophone-recorded sounds can be digitized and played back, and added to the file of a specific whale if it be known. This gives us the capability of analyzing the call of individual whales, for possible signature information, and classifying the types of calls or songs by frequency and amplitude modulation. The system will also keep logs on all video, film and sound recordings, for bookkeeping and cross reference. Ultimately the system has the ability to become the nexus for real-time data collection, with notes, video, sound, position and time being recorded simultaneously while we are observing humpback behavior in the field.

Though the system is new, our first season of testing has proven to be highly successful. Our expectations have been met, and the result is a far more productive field season and a more comprehensive understanding of the humpback whale.

46 Tail submerging (left) *Photographs collected over years give insight into patterns of behavior for individual whales. Information such as calving intervals, feeding and breeding site fidelity, group formations, and migratory routes, are some of the essential pieces of the puzzle we are able to fit together through long-term photo-identification. In this photograph, the author captures a tail on film just as it submerges for a deep dive. The island in the background is Five Finger Lighthouse, which was the last U.S. lighthouse on the West Coast to remain manually operated, before it became mechanized in 1983 (photo by Russ Nilson).*

47 "Droopy flukes" *The shape or drape of the tail flukes also varies among whales. This whale we named "droopy flukes" because of the beautiful drape of the flukes when sounding.*

48 Dorsal scarring *Aside from the white to black pigmentation patterns on the ventral surface of the flukes, the dorsal scarring on the flukes is diagnostic. The tooth scars of a killer whale can be seen on the right lobe of this whale. Killer whale tooth scarring is noted in about 30 percent of the whales we observe. Favored target areas of the killer whale are the tail flukes, lips and tongue.*

49 Scalloping *The scalloping on the trailing edge is as unique to each whale as it is to humpbacks in general. Those patterns are diagnostic, although more so if the flukes have cuts or bites out of them. This whale has killer whale tooth raking on both the dorsal and ventral surfaces. Barnacles at the fluke tips are frequent, but they do not make a good distinguishing characteristic because they change.*

50 Scarring *On the ventral surface the black tail fluke has acquired white markings from killer whale teeth on the left lobe, possibly a bite out of the right lobe, and a distinctive barnacle scar stands alone on the right lobe.*

51–56 Different individual characteristics
*The selection of different tails on this and the
following page shows the distinctive
characteristics of individual whales and the high
variability between flukes. The whale pictured
in plate 56 has a bent tail fluke on the right side.
It is possible that this is due to damage by a
boat's propeller. The deformity is uniquely
identifiable.*

54–56 *See previous page for descriptions.*

57 Tail Characteristics (continued) *Two distinctly different flukes may be observed here as a pair of whales sound. The forward whale has two deep notches of such symmetry that it was probably born with them, and the following whale is nearly uniform in the scalloping along the trailing edge.*

58 Classification *Our computer system enables us to classify whale tails rapidly. Eleven different classification categories are used to sort the patterns. This tail will be sorted for the black marking continuing from the tail stock to the trailing edge, and for the two black markings on the left lobe.*

59 Sorting *The white tail will be sorted into a category which has no black markings from the tail stock to the trailing edge, but does have a black border on the trailing edge only.*

60 Dorsal fin *Individual humpbacks may also be identified by the dorsal fin if it has unique characteristics. By determining these peculiarities during observations, we can identify individuals before they fluke up, an advantage for certain studies. The fluke of this whale is sharply pointed and the dorsal fin pictured has a large mound on which sits a small fin.*

BLOWS

Few features of the great whales are so expressive and so easily observed as the blow. It is these geysers of spent breath, erupting from the surface and billowing skyward, that most often announce the presence of the leviathans. Hanging in the chill Alaskan air, these steamy plumes remind us that whales, like humans, are air-breathing mammals. Blows can reveal many secrets of a humpback's life, if one knows how to interpret them. Because whales are inexorably bound to the surface by the need to replenish their oxygen supply, the sound and pattern of their spouts can yield much information about their activities and emotional states.

The spout of a humpback appearing on the horizon can usually be distinguished from that of other whales by its thick plume and tall "inverted pear" shape. On calm cool days, humpback spouts may loom 20 feet high and drift in the air for several minutes before they dissipate. This plume height results from tremendous pressure within the lung cavity, that forces the blow out at speeds approaching 300 miles per hour. As the warm, pressurized air is forcefully expelled into the cool atmosphere, it expands rapidly and condenses, creating the large plume of vapor. Occasionally, two streams of vapor can be seen issuing from a humpback's nostrils, revealing the paired blowholes peculiar to all mysticete whales.

A remarkable aspect of the humpback's blow is that it reflects with some precision the depths to which the whale descends while foraging. Relatively shallow dives of less than 100 feet are indicated when the whale spouts one, two or three times at the surface, and subsequently sounds for only a few minutes. In contrast, a whale that blows many times at the surface, and then dives for periods of five minutes or more, has gone to greater depths for its prey.

At all activity levels, the rush of escaping air past the humpback's nostrils produces a loud "whooshing" sound. The subsequent inhalation however is rarely audible, and generally takes only a fraction of a second. During exhalation, humpbacks can produce a variety of different sounds that provide additional information about their behavioral and emotional states. Commonly heard in exhalation are wheezed blows that appear to be deliberate, and that may even be a means of communicating. These wheezed blows are most commonly produced by excited whales that are actively feeding, or are involved in some vigorous social activity. On occasion, extremely loud trumpet blasts are sounded by highly stressed or excited humpbacks. These blasts, amazingly similar to those of an actual trumpet, are sometimes heard during feeding episodes, or when humpbacks are agitated by the presence of killer whales.

61 Blowing whales *Marine mammals, like land mammals, are air breathing and are therefore dependent upon access to the water's surface to survive. The beautiful plume can be seen for miles and can reveal not only the whale's presence but also its behavior. After a heavy feeding bout, lasting over five hours, two humpbacks break off from the group to rest. Moving slowly in tandem, they remain primarily on the surface blowing in synchrony, which indicates that they are resting rather than foraging or sleeping. Foraging generally involves more mobility and longer dive times, whereas a sleeping whale hangs at the surface, raising its head occasionally to blow once, then resuming its nap sometimes in total oblivion until it is time to breathe again. Whales usually sleep individually but are occasionally observed taking "cat-naps" together.*

62 Blows (overleaf) *Whales blowing all around us.*

The human observer should avoid either breathing in the blow or coming into contact with the vapor, as it may on occasion harbor pathogenic viruses and bacteria. Cameras and other optical equipment should also be kept away from the whale's breath, for the oil in the tiny droplets is difficult to remove from a lens.

63 & 64 (bottom right) Rainbows *On cool days the condensation of a blow is more highly visible, yet on sunny days the blow can create beautiful rainbows, lasting only the brief moments that the blow lingers, depending on the strength of the wind.*

64 *Rainbows*

65 Blows *The distinctive pear-shaped blow of the humpback can reach heights of 20 feet and speeds of 300 m.p.h. A whale that blows numerous times at the surface and then dives for five minutes or more indicates a deep dive. One to three blows and a brief sounding indicate a shallow dive of less than 100 feet.*

BREACHING

The breaching of a great whale is one of the most dramatic statements of power in the animal kingdom. The fact that it so often happens without any warning adds much to its thrill and impact.

One morning, when a heavy blanket of fog hung over Frederick Sound, Russ and I were adrift in our small outboard-powered boat, recording the dive profiles of feeding whales. Swarms of krill were floating in the water, and a large group of humpbacks had arrived in the area to feed upon them. Ordinarily we would leave our motor idling, so that the whales would be aware of our presence, but on this occasion the scene was altogether too peaceful for us to make such a discordant noise. The whales blew once, maybe twice, then lifted their flukes for a shallow dive. Again they surfaced, blew, and lifted their flukes to dive. Everywhere we looked whales were blowing and fluking up, feeding on the krill that had stayed near the surface on this foggy day. There was something fantastic, surreal and dreamlike about the scene.

We were so completely engrossed in our work that when 90,000 pounds of whale rocketed straight out of the water, not more than twenty feet away, I nearly dropped dead with astonishment. They say that time stands still in moments of terror. I recall staring straight up at all of those 50 feet, watching an animal the size of a small locomotive waver over us, as if deciding which way to fall. Whether by design or not, the whale fell away from our tiny boat, but the wave it threw up when it crashed back into the water nearly sank us all the same. A moment later, the sea had swallowed whale and wave again, and scarcely a ripple remained as witness to our narrow escape.

Our unexpected presence was undoubtedly the cause of this breach. It might have been better to leave the motor idling despite the noise. Whales do not like surprises. Thus I know of four accidents involving kayaks and whales, because kayaks are so quiet that they can come upon a whale unaware, provoking startled and sometimes dangerous reactions. In oceanic research the utmost care must always be taken not to startle or alarm the whales. This is both out of respect for the great animals in whose domain we are the intruders, and also out of concern for the safety of the researcher. Should a whale become annoyed, then a breach can be a very explicit expression of the fact. Forty tons of whale leaping 50 feet in the air make a statement it is best not to ignore.

No other aspect of whale behavior has received so much attention and speculation as the topic of breaching. At first glance, breaching appears to be an exuberant form of play activity, and undoubtedly it is often just that. Yet

66 Breaching (right) *A humpback breaches while* Acania *stands off.*

there are many different types of breaches, and just as many distinctive occasions when a breach is likely to occur. The most impressive is the full body breach, in which the whale completely leaves the water. Probably to protect the more delicate ventral region, the humpback will launch through the surface in a rotating movement, so as to land on its side or its back. Less spectacular breaches, such as the chin slap, in which the animal rises only partially out of the water, often result in a belly landing, with much less impact than a full breach.

There are many reasons why whales breach, but increases in windspeed and heavy seas make it more likely. The reason for this is unclear. It may be that wind-generated noise interferes with more subtle forms of communication. As with other forms of percussion, the sound of a whale colliding with the surface can radiate for a considerable distance, both above and below the waves. The way in which a whale lands can very much influence the character and force of the concussion. Many breaches at close range are inaudible over the hydrophone, while others that are more distant are far more easily heard. Perhaps, by varying the way they hit the water's surface, whales are able to encode the sounds with various information.

Whales also seem to respond to some sounds with a breach. One specific tug and barge that we often see seems to provoke this response, and one particular cruise ship invariably leaves a trail of breaching whales. Whether the whales are responding to the noise of the engine or of the propeller is not clear, but the Navy is able to determine

67 & 68 Breaching *The reason for a breach must be understood within the context in which it occurs. What appears to be simply exuberance may actually be a different response altogether. Separation from a group may be one reason. High winds, irritation or harassment are other causes, and calves tend to breach more often than adults. The element of surprise is one situation that causes a breach. Whales, like everyone else, don't like being taken by surprise, and silent kayakers sometimes meet with unexpected responses such as breaching or tail slaps when catching a whale unaware.*

69 Double breach *Two whales unexpectedly breach in perfect synchrony. Though we have seen even three whales do so, we have never been able to capture it on film. That they are capable of such precision suggests that they are in good control of their actions and may even be able to encode information in the way that they land.*

70–72 Variations of breaching *Breaches vary in their intensity from full-body breaches, when the animal leaves the water entirely, to chin slaps, in which the humpback rises partially and drops back with a smack. This usually occurs with whales that have breached repeatedly and appear to be growing fatigued, and calves who seem to be experimenting with variations or levels of expertise.*

specific boats from the "prop signature" and perhaps the whales are able to do the same, finding some "signature" noises more irritating than others.

Breaching activity is also associated with social interaction, such as the forming and disbanding of humpback groups. Although affiliation and disaffiliation between individuals and groups is usually informal and undramatic, occasionally a whale approaching a group may announce its arrival with a breach, or likewise it may be rebuffed with some sort of surface commotion. A single spirited breach is sometimes executed at the end of an episode of cooperative lunge feeding, when a whale separates from the group. At other times, a breach will cause the entire pod to disaffiliate. Calves breach far more readily than do adults, perhaps because of youthful exuberance. As in all young animals, such friskiness develops skills and coordination, strengthening the muscles, and ultimately preparing the young for independence from the mother. It has also been suggested that the mother, as she distances herself from the calf by weaning, breaches as a method of separation. Breaching may also be a means of maintaining hygiene by aiding in the removal of dead skin, parasites or barnacles. Remarkably enough, we have even seen breaching used as a means of manipulating prey. One whale in Frederick Sound devised the spectacular feeding technique of breaching and

73–76 Full breach sequence *In a spectacular display, a breaching 50 foot whale hurtles into the air, displacing 90,000 pounds of water as it lands. A whale almost always lands on its side or back, presumably to avoid shock to the internal organs which are near the delicate ventral region.*

then immediately swimming through the area in a lateral orientation with its mouth agape. Probably he was at the same time stunning the prey and creating a vortex by the fall, which concentrated the prey. However it worked, it must have been effective, for the whale continued in this manner for quite some time.

As with all animal behaviors, a breach can only be fully understood in the context within which it has happened. Time and plentiful observations will allow explanations to emerge, giving credence to one theory while disproving another. The search for understanding why whales act as they do and when they do has been a large part of our work. Yet these great creatures remain so shrouded in mystery that many of our theories are still little more than educated speculation.

77–79 Lower breaches (left) *A humpback may breach as many as twenty times in succession, but as it grows weary the breaches become much lower in the water until eventually they cease altogether. Because the* *expenditure of energy must be tremendous, even when the cause of the breach is not obvious it can be assumed that there is a social significance.*

SPYHOPS, SLAPS AND LOBS

SPYHOPS

When a whale slowly emerges vertically out of the water to about eye level and makes a curious inspection, the behavior is known as spyhopping. Human activities are one reason why humpbacks spyhop. Startling the humpbacks, or otherwise attracting their curiosity, can cause them to perform this distinct maneuver. When a humpback spyhops suddenly at close quarters it can be a truly staggering experience. The sheer immensity of a 40-ton humpback, combined with its remarkable rostrum of sensory nodules and heavy encrustation of barnacles, can be an alarming sight.

As the humpback gives you a probing glance, the kidney-shaped pupil can be seen rotating to and fro in its eye socket. Since their eyes are situated on the extreme opposite sides of their heads, humpbacks may spyhop with their ventral pleats directly toward you, so that they can place you in their stereoscopic field of vision. Spyhopping humpbacks do not always raise their eyes out of the water, however, so it appears that they are able to investigate boats and their occupants by peering through the surface layers.

They most probably possess good vision both in the air and below the surface. The ability to see well in both these elements may be partially attributed to the bifocal capabilities of their eyes. A circular "fish-eye" lens helps them to cope with the refractive index of water, while in the air good vision may be achieved by rolling the eyes back to view through the flattened portion of the cornea. Additional adaptations to the marine environment include a thickened covering of the eye, so that it will remain rigid when submerged, and a shock-absorbing tissue, lining the socket, that further buffers the eye from pressure changes.

Spyhopping may serve the whale in a number of different ways. We have observed humpbacks that were incorporating spyhopping into a rare and peculiar feeding behavior. It seems that vortices set up by spyhopping through surface layers of krill may concentrate these small creatures into the eddies that swirl as the whale sinks back down. The prey is then promptly engulfed by the cavernous mouth during resurfacing. Some researchers theorize that whales may be obtaining environmental information by spyhopping. Visibility in the water is quite restricted compared to the air, and spyhopping may help whales to orient themselves by scanning the horizon for topographical features, such as mountains or sea cliffs.

As with breaching, so the key to understanding any whale behavior is being able to make comparisons between species, and to study the activities in the particular context in which they occur. A spyhopping whale is a remarkable sight, but the reasons why a whale chooses to lift its head perpendicularly out of the water to eye level are still far from being completely within our grasp.

Our cook aboard *Varua* once had a memorable experience when a curious whale swam under the ship and surfaced next to the galley porthole in a spyhop. While he was baking bread, the cook noticed it had grown dark in the galley. He looked out the porthole straight into the huge eye of the curious beast, less than five feet away. He raced on deck just in time to see it sink back to the briny deep after having scrutinized the galley for over 15 seconds. Apparently satisfied with what he saw, the inquisitive humpback didn't come back to repeat the inspection.

80 Spyhopping (right) *A spyhopping whale unexpectedly raises its head up to peer at my boat. Spyhopping is generally regarded as a curious inspection rather than an antagonistic response. The whale raises its head partly above the water, then gently submerges. Spyhopping may be used in a number of contexts from navigation to locating prey. In Alaska we have witnessed, though rarely, humpbacks using spyhopping as a feeding strategy. It appeared that they were taking advantage of the prey caught in the vortices created by the submergence of their bodies.*

PECTORAL FIN SLAPS

The musical repertoire of the humpbacks is impressive and varied. Not only are these whales great vocalists, they also use their immense fins as instruments of percussion with the sea as a drum. The scientific name of the humpback, *Megaptera novaeangliae*, or "big-winged of New England", refers to the immense flippers or pectoral fins that are one-third as long as the animal's body. No other whale species has flippers that can compare with these, and that distinction makes the humpback easily recognizable.

The humpback uses its long, graceful flippers in many ways—for locomotion and maneuvering, for manipulation of prey in feeding techniques, and for making sounds. The pectoral fins produce a sharp and dramatic report when slapped against the surface. It is not uncommon to see a humpback slapping its pectoral fin on the water for great lengths of time, spending a vast amount of energy in this way.

"Pec slapping" seems to broadcast excitement of some kind, but this may have very different implications depending on the circumstances. Thus a solitary feeding whale may interrupt its foraging to slap repeatedly if approached by another humpback. If a boat comes too close to a humpback, a cautionary slap may be delivered. We have seen circling killer whales warned off by furious slapping, and if this deterrent fails then a barnacle-encrusted pectoral fin will be brandished as a defensive weapon. In each of these circumstances, the pec slap is a warning device that increases in tempo to a threat display if

81 Pectoral fin slapping *A humpback slaps its pectoral fin onto the water's surface. This long appendage, one-third of the total length of the whale, is both an effective weapon against enemies and a good means of broadcasting messages such as territoriality or irritation.*

82   A "Pec Slap" *from a whale is a clear indication to leave the whale alone. Yet a whale will as often direct a pec slap at another whale or simply do it for what appears to be fun. On occasion "pec slapping" occurs for no apparent reason, yet miles away in several directions whales may be observed also engaged in "pec slapping", indicating some level of communication resulting from the auditory report.*

83   Double Pec Slap   *Occasionally a whale rolls over on its back and slaps alternately with both pectoral fins. This seems to occur in periods of extreme agitation and is usually interpreted as a display of submission.*

the warning is ignored.

Pectoral slapping may also act as a spacing mechanism. When a whale sets about spontaneously slapping the surface, humpbacks several miles away may respond with flipper-slapping bouts. This suggests that information is being communicated, such as distance demarcation and possibly the assertion of local feeding rights.

Pec slapping is also used when a whale is aggravated. When irritated, a humpback may give a series of sharp slaps directed at the intruder, whether it be another whale, sea lion, killer whale or man. In particularly fervent action the whale will roll over on its back and slap with both fins one after the other, rocking from side to side and pounding the water in double time with these long flexible fins. This display may indicate submission.

On other occasions, when slowly performed, pec slapping can appear to be a relaxed form of amusement, almost as though it expresses a lazy sense of well-being, particularly among juveniles. Although actual sexual activity in humpbacks has very rarely been observed on either the summer or winter grounds, and thus remains largely a mystery, some of the leisurely pectoral fin waving and caressing we have seen late in the feeding season among close humpback pairs and trios appears similar to the courting behavior displayed by California gray whales.

TAIL LOBBING

Whales have undergone radical modifications in the
process of becoming streamlined enough to glide through a
watery medium 400 times denser than air. With neither
hair to raise on the napes of their necks (even if they had
necks), nor external ears to fold back, nor legs (let alone
tails) to tuck between them, whales lack much of the basic
body language by which terrestrial mammals express
themselves. Instead, whales rely on spectacular movements
of their bodies and extremities to broadcast their intentions
and emotions. Humpbacks are the most acrobatic of all the
great whales, and tail lobbing and slashing is one of their
most frequent and spectacular gestures.

In a typical act of tail lobbing, the humpback lifts its
tail flukes in the air and vigorously slams them on the
water. A frequent variation is the use of the tail stock or
caudal peduncle to pummel the surface. Tail lobbing
sessions may involve a single slap or extend to long
episodes during which the whale hammers away for an
hour or more. The reason for this tail lobbing is not always
evident. Solitary whales swimming leisurely in midchannel
are sometimes seen tail lobbing, in what appears to be
simple playful exuberance. In the case of calves, who tail
lob frequently, coordination and muscular development are
achieved through this carefree play. But for adults, such a
dramatic expenditure of energy should warrant greater
results than simple pleasure. Tail lobbing has a catching
quality, so that one rambunctious whale may cause others
to follow suit. This gives credence to the theory that, like

breaching, the sound of the tail lob may be a means of communication. The sound can travel for a considerable distance both above and below the water, thus advertising the whale's presence. The intensity and quality of the slap will vary considerably, as the whale shifts the angle of flukes and peduncle striking the water. When especially aggravated, a humpback may carry out an inverted tail slap with the ventral surface of the flukes facing upward, a position that possibly makes for more violent impact.

Tail lobbing may also announce the arrival of an individual in a local congregation or the departure of a whale from a group. One possible interpretation for the active tail lobbing of a departed whale is that the whale was actually ostracized from the group and is reacting with irritation, or else an occurrence within the group has caused the irritation. Another reason may be that the whale left the group for the purpose of tail lobbing, perhaps to communicate a message. In some species of toothed whales, tail lobbing is used to herd or stun prey, and some of our observations of feeding humpbacks indicate that they also use tail lobbing to manipulate their prey.

The sideways cocking of flukes and peduncle is generally a sign of an agitated whale. This may be in response to the appearance of predators, to antagonistic interactions with members of its own species, or to the inconsiderate maneuvers of a vessel. On the mating grounds, violent fluke strikes and other acts of aggression are exchanged by males as they battle for access to the females. The barnacle-encrusted flukes of a humpback can become a convincing weapon. Violently slashing the flukes from side to side, the humpback successfully wards off killer whales and sharks or belligerent sea lions and will in the same way express anger at the intrusion of carelessly handled vessels. Despite the immense degree of provocation to which humpbacks are submitted by man, the occasions of their violence or aggression against human beings are rare; but caution, reticence and respect are always the watchwords when moving in their territory. Not only do we owe it to them as their right—it is in our own interests not to tempt fate.

84 Tail slap *A tail slap usually means that the whale is annoyed. The degree to which it lifts its tail is often related to the level of annoyance. The mildest form of a tail slap is a tail lob, in which the whale lifts its tail slightly and abruptly slaps its flukes flat on the water's surface. It is usually delivered only once or twice as a brief message of annoyance. We have also observed tail lobbing used as an unusual feeding strategy. The quick slap may stun the prey or create vortices that force krill into denser concentrations.*

85 Tail slap *The sound produced by the tail's impact upon the water can be heard for miles and may very well be a means of communication. We occasionally see solitary whales tail slapping, which seems to cause whales several miles away to begin tail slapping also. It may work as a territorial display or as a spacing mechanism as well as an aggressive response. A whale may slap as many as 60 times in a tail-slapping session.*

86 Tail slash *A tail slash gives a tail-slapping whale a lateral slice and perhaps more power. It can be seen on the breeding grounds from competing males or on either the breeding or feeding grounds, directed toward annoying boaters, predators or other humpbacks. The cautionary warning of a tail-slapping whale should be heeded for the sake of the whale, as well as for one's own safety.*

87 Inverted tail slap *A tail-slapping whale will occasionally roll over and slap in an inverted position. The musculature of the tail stock enables the whale to slap effectively in either position, yet an inverted tail slap is delivered far more infrequently and may be a submissive posture.*

88 Caudal peduncle slap (overleaf) *A caudal peduncle slap involves an extreme arching of the entire tail stock, then striking the flukes flat on the water with tremendous force and a resounding report. It is usually exhibited by an exceedingly aggravated whale, although it may also be exhibited by an individual departing from a feeding group or even a solitary whale in what is possibly a territorial display.*

FEEDING BEHAVIORS

BASIC STRATEGIES

Humpbacks use a wide variety of feeding strategies to obtain their prey. When an animal employs so many different means to forage, this indicates a catholic taste in food. Humpbacks do not rely on one kind of prey alone, but will feed on whatever is available in sufficient quantities. One essential criterion is that the prey be small enough for the whale to consume; humpbacks cannot swallow anything bigger than a baseball. A humpback has, for example, been found dead with a cormorant stuck in its throat because the bird was too large for the whale to swallow. Yet we have seen those great gaping jaws unintentionally engulf small birds, such as marbled murrelets, and have found the remains of birds in their scat. Essentially humpbacks feed on two kinds of prey—small crustaceans known as krill, and schooling fish such as herring, anchovies, capelin, mackerel, sandlance and juvenile salmon.

As part of our baseline data collection, we have been documenting the different strategies that humpbacks employ to obtain their prey. It is possible to speak of about ten basic strategies, depending on what is considered to be a strategy separate and distinct in itself, for there are many variations on each. Nor are these strategies at all times mutually exclusive; they tend in practice to mingle and overlap. The chosen feeding method is determined according to the prey species, the depth of the prey, the currents and tidal conditions and other environmental factors, and the proximity of other whales. For fast moving prey, like herring, the whales may employ such complex and sophisticated strategies as vertical lunge feeding, vocalizations and cooperative feeding. For slower moving prey, such as krill, solitary feeding is the norm, using horizontal and lateral lunge feeding, bubble clouds or curtains, pectoral sculling, and occasionally flick feeding as appropriate strategies. With more than one whale, echelon feeding is used to capture krill, and for both fish and krill, bubble nets are often employed.

Fidelity to a feeding site is closely related to the abundance of prey. Other factors also influence fidelity, since humpbacks tend to remain in the same general areas over seasons and years. For instance, some man-made disturbances may well have negative effects on feeding site fidelity. Logging efforts or oil exploration may directly or

89 Lunge feeding (overleaf) *The humpback feeds on small schooling fish and shrimp-like crustaceans called krill. In this series of photographs two humpbacks lunge through a school of herring. The pink palatal ridge on the roof of the whale's mouth is visible with the baleen plates hanging in a row from either side. The position of the two whales enables both to benefit. The lead whale, which is in a vertical position, engulfs a large quantity of water and herring, while the second whale receives the escaping herring from the run-off of the first whale and from the currents created by the pair.*

90 Lunge feeding pair (insert) *The lower jaw of the whale opens, creating a vast expanse that can reach 90 degrees. Herring can be seen flying through the air in a last effort to escape the cavernous jaws. This vertically surfacing pair of whales emerged with such tremendous speed that the water is shot out from their mouths as the ventral pleats are collapsed when they sink back into the water.*

indirectly affect whale distribution. We have conducted some studies to determine what effect these human activities may have on feeding conditions. Each year we gain more insight into the complexity of this ecology, as we piece together information about the different factors that influence humpback feeding behavior. Forewarned with such information, we hope to be in a position to avert disasters before any situation gets out of control.

While on the feeding grounds, humpbacks are gentle giants, intent only on meeting their caloric needs. They feed almost constantly, night and day, because the remaining eight months of the year they will fast. It is important that they should not be disturbed while feeding. An animal as endangered as the humpback should remain unmolested, especially during the critical times of feeding and breeding. On the other hand, the humpback itself is also possessed of curiosity, and it will often approach a boat of its own accord, and remain there so long as the boat remains still. We often have humpbacks actively feeding around our ships, completely indifferent to our presence. Indeed the shadow of the ship may actually foster the illusion of protection to the prey, or even attract photo-negative krill, and the humpbacks will take full advantage of these concentrations by feeding around and under the vessel.

91 & 92 Closing the jaw *As the whale closes its jaw on the entrapped prey the water is forced between the baleen plates by the whale's tongue. The water gushes out between the posterior edges of the jaw line, leaving the prey inside.*

93 Closed eyes when surfacing *When surfacing the humpback keeps its eye closed as can be seen in this photograph. This presumably protects the eyeball from the turbulence of the lunge, from escaping fish, and from other whales.*

KRILL

Approximately three-quarters of the diet of the Alaskan humpbacks is composed of tiny planktonic organisms called krill. These small shrimp-like crustaceans occupy a strategic link in the food chain, and are an important prey item for a vast array of predators, including the Cassin's auklet, marbled murrelet, red-necked phalarope and Bonaparte's gull. Several krill species proliferate in the inland waters of Alaska, the most important belonging to the genera *Euphausia* or *Thysanoessa*. These brick-red colored euphausiids spend their entire lives suspended in the water column, feeding on microscopic plankton, which they capture with the interlocking bristles and flaps of their numerous leg-like appendages. With the proper environmental conditions, a massive population explosion can be triggered. The dynamic interplay of light, temperature, salinity, winds, dissolved oxygen, currents, nutrients, coastal runoff, and food availability, greatly influences the productivity and distribution of krill across days, seasons, and years. This constant fluctuation of prey densities has a profound impact on humpbacks, which must frequently dive to differing depths, shift between local feeding sites, or adopt alternate feeding strategies to optimize their foraging success.

Euphausiids are not distributed homogeneously in the water column but occur in massed aggregations similar to schools of fish. Usually they concentrate into dense, horizontal bands that are several feet thick and hundreds of feet long. On fathometers these bands of krill often appear

94 Echelon feeding *Humpbacks may come together in a brief affiliation to lunge in lateral formation. This is called echelon feeding and may involve from two to eight whales, although two to four is most frequent. Each whale benefits from the krill-laden run-off or eddies created by the previous whale. Often the second whale is the first to rise in echelon feeding, as it takes advantage of the eddy created by the preceding whale.*

95 Lateral lunge feeding *is seen when either schooling fish or krill are the prey. The speed obtained in a vertical surfacing can be closely matched in a lateral surfacing, yet the lateral orientation makes it especially effective in covering a greater area. When plowing through the water in a lateral lunge, scooping in krill, a whale may be seen to travel 50 yards in a surfacing before closing its jaw to expel the water.*

96 Sounding for subsurface feeding *Two whales sound for subsurface feeding in Chatham Strait.*

to be located midway in the water column, and are referred to as sonic scattering layers. Some researchers have speculated that the aggregation of krill into these scattering layers is linked with the avoidance of predators, with the location of blooms of phytoplankton upon which they feed, or with the regulation of temperatures required for maturation and reproduction. They may also occur involuntarily as a by-product of currents in the water column.

Euphausiids show a variety of behaviors that appear to help them avoid their predators. One basic characteristic of krill and other sonic scattering layer organisms is their habit of migrating vertically from the surface down to deep levels every few hours. These journeys may help the krill avoid much of the intense pressure of humpbacks and other predators, by sinking away from the surface during the day. At night, or during periods of cloudy weather, euphausiids return to the surface and disperse, to feed in less compact swarms. This is the reason why one may see more humpbacks actively feeding at the surface during the morning or evening than at mid-day.

The abundant *Euphausia superba* that dominates the Antarctic waters has evolved a particularly novel method of predator avoidance. When alarmed, members of the school may deceive a predator by instantaneously molting their shells. The resulting cloud of discarded exoskeletons deceives the predator by acting as a visual decoy, thus permitting the real school of krill to escape. Synchronous molting has not been documented in krill that inhabit Alaskan waters, where their defensive tactic of forming into

97 & 98 Flick feeding *is a very unusual feeding maneuver, employed when krill is near the surface, usually on cloudy, windy days. The whale throws its flukes high as for a deep dive, then gives the flukes a quick flick forward, just before submerging. This forces the krill into denser concentrations as the wave moves over the whale. The whale resurfaces immediately, feeding laterally through the krill, then moves forward and flicks again for the next gulp (photo 98 Fred A. Sharpe).*

99 Pec sculling *One of the more difficult behaviors to understand is the one we call pec sculling. It occurs when a whale is feeding at or near the surface, utilizing one of the several surface feeding maneuvers. The whale for all appearances stops swimming, is hoisted up by its belly and dropped. It is probably doing the reverse of a flick feed, by thrusting the tail down and forward to make an eddy that will concentrate the prey.*

dense schools is protective only against seabirds. On the other hand, this clumping probably makes it easier for humpbacks to detect and engulf the tiny organisms, as is evidenced by the fact that humpbacks descend through scattering layers and consistently target the densest areas of krill. In addition, humpbacks have developed highly sophisticated methods of herding their prey into dense concentrations through the use of bubble nets, clouds, and curtains.

BUBBLE STRUCTURES

Of all the distinctive skills of the humpback whales, perhaps none is more ingenious or useful than their bubble configurations. By discharging air through the blow holes, humpbacks have devised an effective technique with which to herd, concentrate and capture their prey. As the discharged cloud of air rises toward the surface, millions of individual bubbles continuously expand and divide, creating a nebula of effervescence that reduces visibility almost to zero. Depending on how they maneuver and expel the air, the whales can design a variety of bubble traps in the form of nets, curtains or clouds. Both fish and krill are reluctant to swim through these walls of bubbles, and euphausiids may even be lifted by them to the surface.

  In Alaskan waters, the bubble structure most commonly used by humpbacks is the bubble net. Basically, the whale dives below its prey and then swims in circles

100 Resting *After extensive feeding, or when the feeding effort isn't worth the return, whales will rest, sometimes dropping into a deep slumber. Although the head and nares hang below the surface the whale routinely lifts the blowholes for a breath every three minutes or so.*

101 Waiting *A solitary whale, feeding on densely schooling herring, tries patience as a means of capture. This whale held its mouth open for up to 15 seconds while the thick schools swam into the open mouth.*

102 Cooperative feeding *is the most spectacular of all the feeding behaviors. Whales come together in a group to manipulate fast moving schools of fish, a prey species that would not be as effectively caught by an individual. In 1983 Intersea Research was the first to document scientifically that humpback whales feed cooperatively. Photographic and acoustical recordings were made of this spectacular and sophisticated feeding strategy. Each year we have been adding to our items of information concerning cooperative pods.*

while exhaling. The radius of these circles decreases gradually, thus driving the prey into a tighter and tighter column, while the rising cylinder of bubbles effectively seals off all chance of escape. As the humpback spirals around beneath the prey, it rotates its body so that its blowhole always points toward the center of the circle. Instead of emitting the net in a continuous stream, the humpback releases the bubbles in 15 to 20 pulses that merge to form a continuous cylindrical curtain.

The nets in Alaskan waters are made in a clockwise direction most of the time (it is not known whether such nets are made counter-clockwise in the southern hemisphere, nor even whether they are deployed there at all). A humpback can blow its own private net that may be only 15 feet in diameter, or it may deploy a gigantic purse that is nearly 80 feet wide, big enough to accommodate a large group of lunge-feeding whales. When the whale is foraging on krill, bubble nets are typically used by only one or occasionally two individuals to a net, and the net generally contains three or more revolutions. It is something of a marvel that a 50-foot humpback can consistently swim in such a tight radius while blowing the bubble net. To accomplish this, the whale is probably swimming in an almost vertical position, with head up and tail down in the water and ascending in a corkscrewing manner.

Bubble clouds are made by a massive release of air and are generally associated with foraging on krill. These lime-green mushroom clouds apparently aid the whales in feeding by driving the prey to the surface or by

103 Feeding along a current shear *When two masses of water meet, or currents form over a shallow shoal, a current shear is created. The upwelling along a current shear brings nutrients to the surface, which makes an ideal feeding condition for the humpback. Here a whale swims along a current shear. On a sunny day, when the light is the brightest, the euphausiids travel deep in the water column. In response the whales will either feed deep or rest. Whales that are feeding deep will surface for five or more blows, then submerge for up to 10 minutes in a long dive to depths of up to 100 fathoms.*

concentrating krill within or around the margins of the cloud. The humpback then scoops up the prey by lunging through the middle of the cloud or by gleaning the krill from around the edges. It may also release the cloud at depth and then, rising faster than the cloud, capture the prey that has been sandwiched against the surface. These underwater "cloudbursts" may be used sporadically during lunge feeding when a pod is pursuing schools of herring. Occasionally a dome-shaped cloud is seen in the net just as the whales are surfacing; perhaps this acts as an inner spring to lift the prey to the surface.

Humpbacks fashion linear curtains far less frequently than nets or clouds. After blowing a curtain, the whale swims back along its length, presumably collecting the trapped prey. Sometimes a fine trail of bubbles can be seen creeping up to the surface. This is probably produced unintentionally by the whale and can be quite useful in tracking the whale's underwater movements on calm days.

LATERAL LUNGE AND OTHER FEEDING TECHNIQUES

As dusk falls, a distinct change occurs in the feeding behavior of the humpbacks. In the fading evening light, the krill layer has gradually crept up to the surface, and the humpbacks adjust their feeding strategy accordingly. Instead of raising their flukes into the air for a deep dive, they now skim the prey concentrated at the surface by rolling over onto their sides with their mouths agape. This behavior is called lateral lunge feeding, and is one of the most popular humpback strategies for browsing on krill. The lateral orientation refers to the pitch of the whale's jaw in relation to the water's surface. Plowing through the water in this manner, a humpback can travel nearly 50 yards in a single lunge.

When krill is abundant, several humpbacks will come together to lateral lunge in a formation known as echelon feeding. Upon surfacing, the whales are lined up in a staggered diagonal rank with timing so precise that each whale follows the preceding whale after only a moment's delay. This strategy most often appeals to groups of two to four, but occasionally as many as eight humpbacks will form a diagonal line, and plow through a cloud of krill like a row of harvesters threshing a field of wheat. Although these linear pods are very temporary, it does appear that certain individuals will frequently place themselves in the lead, even though the lead position is apparently not the best. Usually the second whale in line is the first to surface, and each humpback down the line apparently benefits from the

104 Bubble nets (overleaf) *are often employed by a cooperative pod. The net is blown to the exact size of the group of whales that will surface in it. The herring are unable to escape through the net of bubbles and so are forced to the surface. Just before the whales break the surface with their huge open mouths, herring can be seen flying through the air in a last effort to escape the confines of the net and their ultimate fate (photo Fred A. Sharpe).*

temporary concentration of prey that escapes the animal just in front. In addition, the tremendous gape of a whale's mouth in lateral lunge feeding will interrupt the hydrodynamic efficiency of its body. This disruption sets up eddies that whirl the krill into local densities which the next whale in line promptly engulfs.

Humpbacks have a tendency to roll over onto their right sides to feed, though they do sometimes feed on their left sides. This right-sided tendency is not restricted to humpbacks. In the fin whale, lateral lunge feeding on the right side of the body is so evolved that the entire body coloration is asymmetrical. Bottlenose dolphins in the salt marshes of Connecticut are also habitual right-side feeders. These ingenious dolphins capture fish by chasing them out of the water onto muddy banks, sliding through the mud on their right sides to consume the stranded prey. Gray whales too will customarily roll over onto their right sides while vacuuming prey off the bottom, a practice resulting in eroded baleen plates on the right side of the mouth.

Flick feeding is another strategy that humpbacks employ when krill lingers at the surface. The distinctive forward splash of this technique makes it recognizable from a considerable distance. Similar to feeding vocalizations and bubble nets, flick feeding is used to concentrate prey into denser aggregations for each lunge feeding maneuver. The whale does this by arching its flukes high into the air, as if it were gathering momentum for a particularly deep dive. The instant that the base of the flukes starts to slip below the waves, the humpback swiftly flips its tail forward, producing a distinctive concave splash. There are

105 & 106 Bubble nets *By expelling air through their blowholes, humpbacks can create fish "traps" in the form of bubble nets, clouds or curtains. Here the whale has encircled either krill or schooling fish into a net. The whale will surface shortly after the net is completed, in either a vertical or horizontal maneuver, depending on where the prey was consumed within the net. A horizontal surfacing would indicate subsurface feeding, whereas vertical surfacing would be likely to mean surface consumption.*

probably two ways in which this helps to concentrate the krill. As the whale whisks its flukes forward, it wafts the krill into denser aggregations, by the wave it creates below the surface of the water. The flukes may also act as a shovel to scoop up the krill-laden water and toss it forward to the spot where the whale's mouth will surface. Timing is very critical to this maneuver. We have seen whales mistime the flick and end up with an ineffectual swipe at empty air, but, undaunted, the humpback will remain in the same position, and quickly recoil its flukes to take another shot. Flick feeding, which is a rather rare feeding behavior, occurs in low-light situations when krill is at the surface. It also occurs with lateral lunge feeding.

Pectoral sculling is yet another unusual behavior used when feeding on krill. It is an odd-looking technique wherein the whale appears to be hoisted up by its belly and dropped back down again. In reality, the whale is using its pectoral fins in conjunction with its tail to create vortices to concentrate the prey. As the flukes are thrust downward, the pectoral fins scull backward, then forward, and the back of the whale rises high in the water for a brief moment before it drops down to engulf the prey.

Probably the commonest feeding behavior is the least dramatic, and can simply be called horizontal surfacing. In this strategy, the whale flukes up for a shallow dive, feeds through the krill layer briefly, and then resurfaces with a quick series of blows. This maneuver is most likely to occur along a current shear, where nutrients and krill are being carried to the surface on the vertical flow of water, or in low-light situations, when the krill layer is close to the surface.

During deep feeding the surface behavior is very similar, but the time that the whale spends submerged is increased. In a dive of over 100 feet the whale will stay submerged for five to ten minutes, then surface with a series of blows. The whale will sometimes take a brief rest, in which it hangs motionlessly at the surface, intermittently raising its blowholes for a breath. After as long as ten minutes on the surface the whale will throw its flukes for another deep dive. Deep diving usually occurs around mid-day when the krill layer is deep down because of the bright lighting conditions.

When feeding on schooling fish, humpbacks employ a variety of sophisticated techniques that will be discussed in the following chapter on cooperative feeding. However there is one very unusual technique that is used when a single whale targets a dense school of fish. We have seen this technique used on herring schooling at the surface in concentrations so thick that they appeared to be boiling, with a sound like pouring rain. Unable to outmaneuver the fish, the humpback surfaces amidst the school, slowly opens its cavernous jaws and patiently sits with its mouth agape for up to fifteen seconds. Perhaps the herring are attracted to the pink palate, or to the dark cavern of the lower jaw, or are simply unaware of the predicament, but when the mouth is sufficiently full the whale quickly closes its mouth. It then submerges and resurfaces slowly in another part of the school, repeating the maneuver until the school of herring eventually disperses.

COOPERATIVE FEEDING

The humpback's subtle and ingenious methods of catching prey are just as dramatic and expressive of a complex intelligence as its prodigious acrobatics. Yet there remains one more feeding behavior that in our view is perhaps the most remarkable of all. For the past eight years, we have been recording, documenting, and collecting data on cooperative feeding. This is one of the most complex behaviors in the animal kingdom, certainly one of the most astonishing, and with significance for our deeper understanding of the whales. We shall treat cooperative feeding at some length, because until now little has been known about it and because the greater part of what follows here has not been published before.

Cooperation in a common endeavor will transform a loosely associated group of individuals into a complex social unit. There are many potential benefits that individuals may derive from cooperating in large groups, including joint defense against predators, more opportunities for reproduction and greater access to food. For humpbacks on the summer grounds, the fundamental incentive to cooperate is the quest for a more successful hunt. Banding together into large pods allows humpbacks to capture schools of fast, vigilant fish that would otherwise be difficult for solitary individuals to catch. Although browsing on krill calls for fewer complex social interactions, the population levels of this small crustacean can fluctuate widely, and it is therefore not always available. The nutritional value of schooling fish is considerably greater than krill, and this must be significant to humpbacks that have only a few months in which to feed.

Cooperative feeding of humpbacks on schools of fish is strikingly similar to the societal relationships of other predators, as seen in prides of lions, packs of wolves, or pods of killer whales. Having neither the speed of the finner whales nor the maneuverability of the dolphins, humpbacks must cooperate fully in order to chase and capture the fast schooling fish. Thus the purpose of cooperative lunge feeding is to cluster together as many fish as possible in a small volume of water, so that they can all be devoured in one single gulp.

Cooperation in cetaceans has been observed only in several species of toothed whales and in humpbacks. Intersea Research was the first to document scientifically this unusual behavior of the humpbacks. We first observed whales feeding cooperatively in September 1981. When the

107 Cooperative feeding sequences and strategies (overleaf) *To date we have recorded 27 different cooperative pods. We have found that some members of a group remain together consistently over days, months and years, while others are variable and will join with different groups. These observations run contrary to current thought, which is that mysticete whales do not maintain stable relationships over time.*

108–109 Cooperative feeding *What first appears as a chaos of floundering whales is actually a very carefully choreographed maneuver. Every time that this group was photographed, over a three-day period in 1983, the whales maintained the same spatial relationships and physical orientation to one another upon each surfacing.*

behavior was next seen in August 1983, we were working from *Varua* in an area of upwelling along an 80-meter shoal that separates two deep bodies of water. The strong upwelling currents created by this shoaling result in an increased nutrient supply and thus a productive surface layer. Clouds of krill were visible, along with schools of herring so thick that they blackened the water. In this productive area, we observed a group of eight humpbacks feeding in a cooperative manner over a three-day period. Since that time, we have observed thirty-seven different groups cooperatively feeding, and over 1200 coordinated feeding maneuvers.

A lunging bout begins when a pod of humpbacks, swimming at the surface, detects a school of herring either at the surface or at depth. Rather than charging directly at the herring, the whales dive and circle beneath them. From this strategic position, they begin to manipulate the school, through the use of vocalizations and occasionally a gigantic bubble net. In response, the frightened fish form a tight ball, and flee from or are stunned by the piercing vocalization. Because the song is sometimes used without a bubble net, it appears to be the strategic factor involved in the prey manipulation. The circular net, which is used about 30 percent of the time, keeps the fish from moving laterally, and forces them to flee upwards. At the surface, the school attempts to disperse laterally, so it is important that the bubble net reaches the surface before the herring. As the noisy effervescing spiral of bubbles quickly rises around them, the school of herring becomes trapped between the surface and the bubbles. The humpbacks then come rocketing up through the vertical tunnel of bubbles, and the herring boil at the surface in a final desperate attempt to escape. As the whales burst forth, like monsters from the deep, the sea erupts into a boiling cauldron of rostrums, pectoral fins, baleen plates, ventral pleats and spouts, and the panicked herring leap into the air in vain. The two whales at the front of the group have surfaced in a vertical position, and the following whales in a lateral orientation. The prey-laden water that escapes from the mouths of the foremost whales rushes into the mouths of the whales behind, who have surfaced just a fraction of a second later, to take advantage of the run-off of escaping herring. In their cavernous mouths the whales consume the trapped fish, grotesquely distending their ventral pleats and then quickly disgorging the water through their baleen plates. The whole incident from hunt to capture has lasted about five minutes. The whales in most cases then return to the same direction in which they were heading previously, and resume their hunt.

THE CHOREOGRAPHY OF THE MANEUVER
Although at first glance there appears to be no order to the pandemonium of chaotic surfacing, it is actually the choreographed climax to a carefully orchestrated maneuver. One of the most fascinating aspects of cooperative feeding among humpbacks is that a pod maintains the same formation every time it bursts through the surface. Our amazement at this discovery was warranted. This precision of choreography had not been documented elsewhere for baleen whales, nor indeed for

110 Cooperative feeding *The two whales pictured here have been seen together each year throughout the course of the summers since 1983. The cooperative group which is led by the two whales in this picture always maintains basically the same surfacing formation, with variations dependent upon the number of animals comprising the group at any one time. It appears that a social hierarchy is involved in the group structure. The fact that the largest whales maintain the most favorable positions could well indicate that the position is acquired with age and capability or status.*

any whale species. Out of 130 surfacings from the group we worked with in 1983, we were able to record photographically that each whale maintained its own identical position and physical orientation within the pod during every surfacing, thus demonstrating the highly coordinated nature of lunge feeding. This observation also provided the first sonagram analysis of the feeding vocalizations. Our findings were conclusive evidence that the whales were cooperating rather than competing for their prey. Five years later, this group is still surfacing in the same precise formation as in 1983, with the members each maintaining the same location and orientation within the pod.

We have also learned that the sociobiology of humpbacks on the feeding grounds is much more complex than we had supposed. We found that distinct leadership roles are maintained in a pod. The leader typically holds the central place as the group lunges to the surface, and often rises much higher vertically than the other whales. In a study of several pods we were able to show that the whales holding this superior position were also those that had initiated the lunge maneuvers and had made the feeding vocalizations. Although it is not yet possible to state this conclusively as a rule, the evidence does suggest that the lead humpback is often the one that targets the particular herring school for pursuit, that sings the song, and then leads the final assault up through the bubble net.

Leadership is a social characteristic that occurs in a number of long-lived species such as lions, wolves, elephants and humans. Significant survival information may be passed from one generation to the next, so that specialized feeding strategies, prey distribution and seasonal changes may be information which is acquired over time. One pair of large humpbacks, that we named "Mama" and "Rake", maintained their leadership roles despite adopting entirely new pods over the course of a summer. Both Mama and Rake are exceptionally large whales, heavily scarred, with every appearance of being elders.

SOCIAL STRUCTURE

A major aim of our research has been to examine the behavior of cooperative pods, so as to gain some insight into their basic social framework. After our discovery that the pods consistently used the same lunge formation, we developed a number of hypotheses to explain this interesting phenomenon. One was that the forward, lead positions within the lunge formation permitted a larger catch of fish, owing to the strategic central location. Perhaps individuals were competing to retain these rich "territories", in a manner similar to the dominance hierarchy observed in many other animals. Yet we have never seen any overt aggression such as to suggest that these lead positions are won and maintained through competitive interactions. In fact, through our continued observations we have found that there are occasions, admittedly rare, when the leadership of a cooperatively lunge-feeding pod appears to be shared alternately between two whales. When one of these whales is not leading, it takes a secondary position on surfacing. During such a

111 Cooperative feeding *This picture shows a surfacing formation typical of these two lead whales, that have remained together over years.*

situation, the two leader whales will both start their version of the feeding song, singing simultaneously for periods of up to 30 seconds. At that point, one or the other whale will take over as solo. The surfacing will be in one of two distinct formations, depending on which of the two whales was leading.

The singing of two or even three whales that occurs during vertical lunge-feeding maneuvers is fairly common, yet whales have never been heard singing together on the winter calving grounds. This may indicate a degree of involvement and cooperation between the singers, necessary for the effective capture of prey but unlikely to occur during the competitive courtship that occurs on the winter grounds. It may also indicate a confusion in leadership, when leaders from different groups meet within the same group, but more likely it may have a role to play in the manipulation of the prey, as it tends to occur at specific points of the song. Sometimes duetting is heard throughout the entire song, when two whales sing the same song in turn or in perfect unison. This seems to be another carefully orchestrated aspect of the cooperative lunge-feeding maneuver.

Although pods of humpbacks will consistently keep to the same lunge formation, they will greatly modify many other aspects of their cooperative foraging strategy. Our research has shown that the total number of whales in a group, the pattern and sequence in which they dive, the length of time they spend submerged, the depth to which they dive, and the use of bubble nets, can all vary greatly within a single pod or between different pods.

In addition, there are several other important aspects of cooperative lunge feeding that are highly variable. The ability of these pods to alter abruptly their direction of travel, and the intensity with which they engage in lunging, demonstrates a high degree of sensitivity to their environment. There is often no obvious reason for a pod to discontinue and then later resume using bubble nets, or abruptly to disaffiliate, or suddenly to depart from an area after remaining there for several weeks. It becomes apparent that cooperative lunge feeding is not a mindless, stereotyped behavior, but is actually a very carefully arranged event, that requires precise timing and execution. We may assume that in most aspects of feeding behavior all the influencing factors are interrelated but not all are known to us. Ultimately, these behavioral patterns are likely to reflect the relative abundance and physical distribution of schooling fish.

Humpbacks are thought to have excellent hearing. Our studies strongly suggest that most of the time they simply listen passively, but when alerted can detect and locate a school of fish. Researchers Schwartz and Greer suggest that schools of herring generate a variety of sounds. Humpbacks may be able to hear the high-pitched "chirps" and narrow-tone "whistles" of the schooling herring, and the low-pitched hydrodynamic "roars" made when a school suddenly accelerates or abruptly shifts direction. Herring can also produce a lot of splashing noise while they are striking at prey on or near the surface. When one of these herring disturbances erupts, a pod of humpbacks well over a mile away has been seen to make an abrupt change of

112 Cooperative feeding calf *Although it appears as if a tremendous amount of skill and learning is necessary to accomplish these impressive feeding displays, we observe calves of the year equally involved in the cooperative group feeding along with the adults. After several hours of lunge feeding, a calf may move off to roll in the kelp or otherwise amuse itself, while its mother continues to participate in the lunging bout. In this group of seven, three were calves.*

course, and travel swiftly to begin lunge feeding among the splashing fish. The whale pod shifts direction, picks up speed, gives off loud wheezed exhalations, and makes graceful turns as it diverts to meet the herring school. The herring, when threatened, will typically crowd up and take flight, looking like one huge organism. This tactic works well against most enemies such as seabirds, salmon, porpoises, seals and sea lions—all of these being predators that pursue individuals or small groups. However, those same protective measures that serve against most other predators will betray the fish to the humpback. Schooling behavior is no defense when the attacker is so much larger than its prey that it can swallow an entire school at once.

There are days in Southeast Alaska when the herring arrive in schools so large that they darken the surface of the water in all directions. Corresponding with these immense pulses of herring is a dramatic increase in the number of lunge-feeding humpbacks. Productive upwellings of herring can host three or more cooperative pods, which may intermingle or occasionally exchange members. Despite an increased movement of individuals from one pod to the next when prey is plentiful, the degree of exchange is still considerably less than the random affiliations of humpbacks browsing on krill. Associations between humpbacks grazing on krill are typically measured in minutes or hours, while those of whales pursuing schooling fish are measured in days, weeks or years. The two whales previously mentioned, Mama and Rake, that we have photographed over the last six years, have never been seen apart.

113 Surfacing pod *Sitting dead in the water to make acoustical recordings and accurate observations can result in some unexpectedly close calls. A net is not always blown, so gauging exactly where the whales might surface is not always possible. Here a group of nine whales, weighing approximately 700,000 pounds, surfaces next to our small Boston Whaler (photo Jane Yamaguchi). See page 185 "Hazards".*

114 Cooperative pod *In the course of an hour no less than 22 whales joined together to form this cooperative pod.*

We have also observed in larger pods that certain combinations of whales form sub-groups or "cliques" with fairly stable memberships. Exchanges between cooperative groups generally take place when pods are working closely in the same general area, such as along a reef or after periods of inactivity when the pods break up to rest or travel.

VOCALIZATIONS

Another intriguing aspect of cooperative feeding is the repertoire of beautiful, mesmerizing songs, broadcast by the pod during lunge-feeding maneuvers. These extremely loud vocalizations are used to manipulate schools of fish, making them easier to capture. We have already seen how a typical alarm or avoidance response by many species of schooling fish is to withdraw into tight shoals and swim away from the disturbance, and how the humpbacks will then take advantage of this stereotyped flight response by diving below the school and emitting a piercing vocalization. One possibility is that the frightened fish compact into a tight cluster, which makes it simple to encircle them with a bubble net, as the panicked school swims away from the sound source toward the surface. Because the decibel level of the vocalizations is so high, the sound may cause the herring to be momentarily stunned. As soon as the song begins, all fish in the immediate vicinity cease their surface swimming. Are they diving towards an illusion of safety or are they stunned? Because humpbacks can still effectively corral the fish toward the surface when not using a bubble net, it would appear as if the song alone could effectively concentrate the fish. Disorienting the school or stunning them would be a resourceful maneuver.

The feeding song normally lasts from 55 to 90 seconds and is given in a dozen or so short phrases, each lasting from two to five seconds. These phrases are fairly low in pitch (around 500 Hz), precisely in the frequency range at which Pacific herring are most sensitive to sound. The feeding song is essentially in three parts: the primary phrases, the pause and the ascending phrases. The primary phrases comprise most of the song and are in uniform tones, or they may have a beautiful vibrato quality. Then comes a pause that usually lasts from five to fifteen seconds. Its function is uncertain; it may give the stunned or disoriented herring a momentary chance for escape. After this brief moment, the humpbacks once again target them with the final ascending vocalization just before the herring reach the surface. This final part of the song is in three or four ascending phrases, that rise in pitch as the pod approaches the surface. It ceases as they lunge up and out of the water. At the same time, the pause may also be a listening period. While the pod is broadcasting out the feeding song, it probably drowns out any sounds the herring school may be making, subtle sounds that may be important in the final tracking and locating of the prey. A pause would allow the whales to review their position before the final assault.

The overall length of the feeding song, and the number of individual phrases included, can vary somewhat from one lunge- feeding maneuver to the next. These slight

115 Night feeding *It has been believed that whales require light to feed and that vision plays an important role. We have observed cooperative pods feeding long after night has fallen and even on moonless nights we have been able to identify individual whales. We have also recorded the song which is sung by cooperative pods, long into the night, until about 0900 hours, at which time the whales begin resting (see pages 182–183).*

variations may result from the shifting manipulations of the herring as they try their various evasive tactics. The feeding song may also differ in response to changing depths and densities of the schools of prey. We have found that different humpback groups have different patterns to their vocalizations, which may be a song pattern for the individual singing. Unlike the song on the winter calving grounds, the feeding song does not undergo constant change. It is therefore possible to recognize some of the same songs from one year to the next. This ability to recognize the vocalizations of particular whales has been a great help in our effort to determine precisely which individuals are making the vocalizations. As pods have gradually changed their membership, we have been able, by a process of elimination, to identify the singers, and this has eventually led us to suspect that the lead whale is usually responsible for beginning the vocalizations. Also, on occasions when the first whale sounds, the song begins immediately, even while the tail is still in the air prior to the dive. Although rare, this has given us an opportunity for positive identification.

Other interpretations of the feeding song have been proposed, including the theory that it may serve to coordinate group behavior, or to establish dominance within the pod during the lunge maneuver. The song, however, is sometimes omitted entirely, and even then large pods can still be seen lunging in military precision, making abrupt directional changes, or lunging twice in succession and blowing bubble nets. All of this strongly suggests that prey manipulation rather than coordination or dominance is the basic function of the vocalization. On a number of occasions we have seen solitary whales vocalize while feeding, which would again indicate that prey manipulation was the purpose. We have also observed single humpbacks simultaneously vocalize and blow bubble nets, showing that it is possible for one individual to do both at the same time. Even more remarkable is that on one of these occasions the individual was a calf, which was actively engaged in singing, blowing bubble nets and lunge feeding while the mother remained at a distance, feeding less actively and only occasionally using the song. The song possibly plays an extraneous role in keeping the pod together. Often it seems to serve as an assembly call; when a pod temporarily breaks up, individuals may wander off and become scattered over several square miles but, when the feeding song begins, the separated members immediately turn back toward the source of the vocalization and reconvene.

POD MEMBERSHIP AND LIMITATIONS

While it is clear that cooperation allows humpbacks to exploit food that might otherwise be largely unavailable to them, important questions still remain. For example, as more whales join a lunge-feeding group, does this significantly increase the capture success for each individual in the pod? Is there a level at which the pod becomes too large, and the foraging efficiency of the group starts to decline? As in most aspects of cooperative lunge feeding, the answers to these questions ultimately depend on the local density, distribution and behavior of the prey.

116–122 Cooperative Feeding Sequence *The humpback is famous for its beautiful winter song, yet singing on the summer grounds had almost never been heard. We found that cooperatively feeding whales routinely sing a song prior to surfacing. The vocalization probably serves to manipulate the prey, either by stunning or herding, or by causing the prey to move away from the sound source. We originally believed that the function of the song was to coordinate the group into a precise formation. After observing solitary whales using the song when feeding, and cooperative groups occasionally omitting the song while surfacing in their usual precise formation, we determined that the song was more significant in prey manipulation. We have also found that different groups sing different songs but that the songs remain the same year after year for an individual, enabling us to identify individuals by their vocalization patterns. Only one whale sings at a time, although we occasionally hear*

duets or even trios singing. The song begins
about one minute prior to surfacing and ends
just before the whales break the surface.
Sometimes the song begins while the singer still
has its flukes in the air during the dive. This is
one of the ways we are able to isolate singers
from the group.

Schools of herring can be so thick that they
blacken the water's surface. When the humpback
whale begins the feeding song, all surface
motion of the herring stops within several
hundred meters. Once the whales lunge, the
herring resume their surface schooling. A
"song", as defined by W.B. Broughton in
Acoustic Behavior of Animals *(Elsevier, London,*

*1963), is "a series of notes, generally of more
than one type, uttered in succession and so
related as to form a recognizable sequence or
pattern in time." Based on this definition we
refer to the repetitive sound patterns of feeding
whales as "songs".*
The theory that the whales are competing for
prey is not valid. As can be seen throughout the
following photographs, the whales have plenty of
room to move elsewhere. It is not that the prey is
limited so that competition is necessary, it is that
the whales can work together more effectively
than individually, when feeding on the fast
moving schools of fish.

Schools of herring may withdraw into larger shoals when frightened by the feeding vocalization, so that a larger bubble net would be advantageous to the whales. When prey is abundant, a large net that is properly deployed can corral a phenomenal volume of fish. When schooling fish are plentiful, several pods may work closely together, each singing its song independently of the other group. Occasionally the pods will merge into a super pod which then sings only one song, and surfaces in a single impressive lunge. One pod, which we watched come together over the course of an hour, consisted of twenty two individuals including four calves, and remained feeding together for more than three hours.

In order for any member of the pod to share in a tremendous catch, all whales must cooperate. The herring forced to the surface within the confines of the net are evenly distributed, so that all the member whales should therefore receive adequate amounts of prey. We have observed cooperative pods abandon an area of moderate prey concentrations, and head for schools of herring so dense that they darkened the water for over a quarter of a mile. Even when the pod has dispensed with the bubble net in such dense concentrations, the whales have kept their precise formation when surfacing. Such observations give further support to the theory that the whales are cooperating rather than competing, for the sheer size of such a herring school would mean adequate prey for all whales within a sizable territory. Obviously the whales were maximizing the benefit through their cooperative association.

Several patterns of behavior suggest that the members of a lunge-feeding pod tolerate and even welcome new recruits. As indications of this, we note that solitary humpbacks are strongly attracted to lunging pods by the feeding song and general surface commotion, also that there is no noticeable aggressive interaction when a whale joins or leaves a feeding group. When a bubble net is used, it constantly expands, making room for new arrivals. Overall, the very nature of this feeding method makes for greater success as more whales join the effort.

Although cooperative pods have fairly stable memberships, it is unlikely that they represent extended family units, as is the case with killer whales and elephants. Membership changes as whales gradually shift from pod to pod throughout the feeding season. Some pairs of whales form stable associations that endure for whole summers and even for years, but pods as such do not exhibit a level of cohesion that would suggest strong ties of kinship between the members. We do however see the same individuals cooperatively feeding each year, regardless of their group association. More likely than kinship is fidelity to a feeding area and technique. Yet because new calves are adding to the numbers of cooperative whales annually, it seems reasonable to assume that some kinship ties do exist, but to what extent will have to be determined over time.

DISAFFILIATION OF PODS
Disaffiliation most often seems to be related to changes in the availability of prey. Other factors that may prompt a member to leave, or a group to split up, include a shift in

tidal speed or direction, a change in light conditions, the
arrival of unwelcome killer whales, or simple exhaustion
and satiation after a prolonged session of lunge feeding.
One member may suddenly depart, or the entire pod may
abruptly split up into smaller subgroups that wander off in
different directions.

   If there are several lunge-feeding teams working a tight
area, individuals or small subgroups will occasionally leave
one pod and join another. An individual whale may
increase its foraging success by finding a pod that has more
promising positions available, or that has a more
experienced leader. A pod that is not having much luck at
capturing fish will evidence an increase in aborted and
regular surfacings. Mothers with calves tend to break off
from the group more frequently, but they routinely spend
long hours with the group. Some pairs and subgroups will

wander off together on a regular basis. All of these kinds of behavior can yield valuable clues to the whales' social relationships.

It is not uncommon to observe some form of ritualized behavior, such as breaching or grunting bouts, immediately prior to the dissolution of a pod. Disaffiliation will usually bring about an abrupt change in behavior and may often result in whales departing from a feeding area.

Killer whales are one sure reason for a lunge-feeding pod to break up, particularly when one of the humpbacks becomes a target. In July 1987 we observed three killer whales attack a calf that was a member of a cooperative pod. Two adults remained to assist the calf, but the rest of the pod disbanded.

When a whale has left a group it will tend to move directly out to mid-channel and away from prime feeding locations such as reefs, islets, shorelines and bays. While resting, the whale tends to move to deeper water to get "sea room"—a technique well known to mariners which avoids the accidents of running aground or becoming stranded. In addition, individuals may find it easier to hear the vocalizations and surface activity of renewed lunging activity if they move into mid-channel, away from the shadowing influence of reefs, islands and other land forms.

A cooperative pod will maintain close formation for hours on end, as it dives and lunges through the surface. It is somewhat unusual for any group of predators to maintain such close ranks during the entire time they are detecting, pursuing and capturing their prey. However, nighttime observations of Amboselli lions made by Flip Strickland

indicate that individuals adopt and learn specific rules in the kill. If one of the members is impaired, dies or is not participating, the members rotate in their respective roles, indicating a clear cognitive appreciation of what they are doing. Such social behavior is strikingly similar to the cooperative feeding of humpbacks.

A pod of dolphins, searching for prey, will travel abreast and fan out into broad schools. These laterally spread schools can scan a wider swath of sea for food and enemies, and make it possible for more individuals to take part in the hunt. Once prey is located, the dolphins will contain it by encirclement or herd it by slapping their flukes on the surface. In comparison, the close formation adopted by lunge-feeding humpbacks would seem to waste the talents of those in the middle of the pod. However, the sensory input of the individuals at the center may be less crucial since it appears that the pod is under the guidance

119&120 (overleaf) *Cooperative Feeding*

of a single leader. Moreover, humpbacks lack the speed and maneuverability that enable the dolphins to herd and encircle their prey even though they are in a dispersed formation. Humpbacks have compensated well for these comparative deficiencies by the diligent use of bubble nets, by feeding vocalizations, and by cooperative behavior to capture schooling fish.

As the feeding activity waxes and wanes, a number of changes can be observed in the cooperative pods. During spirited bouts of lunging activity, the pod becomes more excited; it draws closer together, increases its traveling speed and respiration rates, and produces more wheezed blows and trumpet calls. Lulls in feeding activity are characterized by an increase in non-lunge and aborted surfacings, decreased speed and respiration rates, increased spacing between individuals, and an increase in temporary disaffiliations and resting periods.

NIGHTTIME FEEDING *(See page 169)*

There is a widely accepted myth that humpbacks stop feeding when darkness falls and then start again at dawn. By spending a number of nights out on the inky waters, we have found to the contrary that humpbacks continue feeding even in total darkness. At dusk, strategies such as echelon and lateral lunge feeding seem to be preferred, probably in response to a rising layer of krill. As the night grows darker, we have used a bright spotlight to observe that humpbacks are still capable of cooperatively feeding with as much military precision as they exhibit during daylight hours. Snorts, wheezed blows, respiration patterns, and the splashing of feeding humpback whales, may be heard throughout the night. Even more remarkable are the recordings we have made of feeding vocalizations which occur in total darkness. On some nights, the sounds

121 *Cooperative Feeding*

of the feeding song drift through our hull for hours. Bubble nets are also deployed in total darkness. Schooling fish have been shown to respond to bubble screens either by the pressure changes or perhaps the bubbling noise itself, which may serve to frighten or corral the fish.

In 1988, we observed two groups of whales that returned to the same bay for four consecutive nights to continue their cooperative feeding. Though there was some association between the two groups, for the most part they worked independently of each other and returned independently to this one small bay, after traveling as much as 100 miles throughout the day. The deep bay, surrounded by ledges, made an ideal environment for herring, and each night the bay was teeming with fish. By morning the herring dispersed and the whales began resting.

What is extraordinary about this observation is that the

whales were capable of such remarkable sensitivity to their environment. As dusk fell they would head directly for the bay, to get there by dark, and on one occasion they traveled 25 miles in four hours to do so. The whales were not feeding out of convenience, but rather were targeting with remarkable alacrity a known prolific area that was either detected or remembered.

The fact of cooperative feeding at night raises intriguing questions about how humpbacks are able to locate and capture their prey in total darkness. Foraging in the dark lends credence to our conclusion that these whales possess incredibly sensitive hearing, since hearing is the sense most likely to be used for nocturnal feeding. It is also quite possible that the sensory nodules, and vibrisal or snout hairs, play an important role in detecting patches of prey in the water or in maintaining lunge formations. During the day, humpbacks will dive well below the lighted

122 *Cooperative Feeding*

zone, so it is possible that sensory nodules are helpful in these situations also.

HAZARDS OF RESEARCHING COOPERATIVE PODS *(See page 165)*
Many of the foregoing observations were made from the bow of *Varua* or the deck of *Acania*. Never do we deliberately intrude ourselves upon the whales; nor do we interfere with their activities. Our studies are all conducted unobtrusively, both out of respect for the whales themselves and because our research is concerned with the observation of non-manipulated natural behaviors. However, to record the vocalizations that are such an important part of cooperative feeding, it is necessary to launch a small boat that can work in silence at a considerable distance from the mother ship.

When a small boat is sitting dead in the water, problems may arise. Whales are very much aware of what is going on around them, but they rely to a great extent upon their hearing, and once they begin feeding they tend to ignore anything other than the capture of their prey. Many a time when sitting quiet in the water I have accidentally taken a solitary feeding whale by surprise. On the other hand, there have also been times when a cooperative feeding group has taken me by surprise.

On one such occasion, I was sitting in our 13-foot Boston Whaler observing a group of nine whales as they worked together over the reef. My boat was dead in the water with a hydrophone over the side. It was a quiet day with not a breath of wind to disturb the glassy water or the heavy air. Whales were swimming along the surface, leisurely blowing their peaceful blows as they foraged for prey. Locating a dense school, they would exhale more forcefully and one by one fluke up and disappear. Sometimes as many as five minutes passed before the eerie vocalizations began. While the whales were singing, I scanned the placid water for any sign of where they might surface. Sometimes they blew a bubble net simultaneously with the song, and then I knew for sure where they would come up. More often there was no sign at all, except in that fraction of a second before they emerged, when thousands of herring flew into the air in a last attempt to escape. The whales would then burst through the surface in a powerful lunge with mouths wide open. Those herring that escaped the jaws of one whale fell victim to the next, as the water from the immense jaws rushed from whale to whale. Their huge ventral pleats were expanded with the intake, then the expelled water gushed out through the baleen plates. The turbulence diminished as the whales resumed their search, and once again fluked up for another encircling of their prey. Over and over again the performance was repeated as they tirelessly worked the productive reef. Each time I guessed fairly accurately where they would surface, always trying to keep a safe distance.

The day had been long. I was parched and burnt after many hours out in the small boat, and decided to head back to the ship. The whales had been down for a long time, and then I began to hear the song without the aid of the hydrophone. At once all of the nearby herring stopped their surface swimming. An ominous silence fell upon the stillness of the day. I had been expecting the whales to surface at least a quarter of a mile away, but the fact that I could hear their song unaided meant that they were near. Nervously I glanced over the side of the boat just in time to see the white flash of pectoral fins racing to the surface. If I wasn't engulfed, I would be crushed. Nine whales together add up to some 700,000 pounds. My little boat weighs 400. The odds did not look good. I grabbed my camera as the whales broke through and snapped a picture—as I thought, my last. Tremendous jaws encased my boat, baleen surrounded me and herring shot through the air, landing at my feet. Within a split second, the whales saw me and they veered, collided, then sank back into the deep. I was left intact, swamped and shaken, amid excited blows all around. Nothing else in my life has ever produced such a combination of thrills, alarms and excitement as working with those pods of humpback whales.

Interactions of Humpbacks with Other Marine Mammals

In the course of our research, we have studied relationships between the humpback whales and their too often troublesome natural neighbors, the killer whale (*Orcinus orca*) and the Steller sea lion (*Eumetopias jubata*).

The killer whale or orca is one of the most misunderstood of all marine mammals. Its habits have long been a mystery, and its reputation has been greatly distorted in both scientific and popular literature. Many early accounts of orcas describe them as fearsome beasts with insatiable appetites. These misconceptions were in part due to the whales' appearance, its menacing eye patches, threatening teeth, and the tall dark dorsal fin that slices ominously through the water. Of course the name, "killer", only adds to our melodramatic notions of danger. The last fifteen years, however, have brought about a shift in our attitudes towards these magnificent creatures. Accounts of their ferocious habits are slowly being replaced by a deep respect and appreciation for their intelligence, amiability and remarkable predatory skills.

Our understanding of the killer whale's behavior and social structure has greatly increased, thanks to our ability

123 Killer whales *The large triangular dorsal fin of the male killer whale may reach a height of six feet, whereas the fin of the female reaches about three feet. We have witnessed three killer whale attacks on humpbacks. The humpbacks' reaction is to assume an inverted posture in which their flukes and rostrum are lifted as high as possible out of the water, and to breathe in a distressed manner, which is a rapid wheezed exhalation, and to slash their tails horizontally across the water surface, and to roll over, probably to protect their delicate ventral regions.*

to identify individuals. This is done by photographing the distinctive shape of their saddle patches and the nicks and scratches on their dorsal fins. Mature males can be recognized by the height of the dorsal fin, which is straight and reaches to six feet. Females and immature whales have much shorter and more curved fins. Males reach a length up to 32 feet, and females typically reach 28 feet. Females spend their entire lives within the same pod. The pod is generally composed of several smaller subgroups, consisting of mothers and their offspring, and it is an extremely stable social entity.

Killer whales possess incredible communicative abilities, and each pod appears to have its own call repertoire or dialect. Although determining the age of these animals is still an uncertain process, researchers believe that the lifespan of females may be at least 70 years, with males living to perhaps 50 years. In the Pacific Northwest there appear to be two sub-populations of killer whales, residents and transients. Killer whales in Alaskan waters are also divided into these two types of sub-populations. The differences between these two types are considerable. In Puget Sound, resident killer whales are known to vocalize extensively, and to prowl open deepwater habitats in search of salmon. In contrast, the larger transients are silent much of the time, as they stealthily prowl along close to shore in search of mammalian prey, such as seals or sea lions. Perhaps the slow swimming and subtle behaviors of the humpbacks when in the presence of killer whales are a means of deterring an attack. Because the killers seem to take such pleasure in harassing other marine mammals, the

124 Steller sea lions *A colony of Steller sea lions hauled out on the Brother's Islands. When a humpback approaches too closely, the sea lions will sometimes leave the beach to harass the whale by swimming around it, and over it, and by nipping at its flukes and flippers (see pages 196-197).*

humpbacks may have learned not to attract attention and to avoid appearing as playful sport.

Killer whales and humpbacks often share the same area, with little reaction from either species. Evasive maneuvers on the part of humpbacks are not always readily apparent; sometimes they do not react at all, perhaps because they are able to tell when the orcas are not searching for prey. Also it may be possible that humpbacks can differentiate between the fish-eating residents and the potentially more dangerous meat-eating transients, and can adjust their behavior accordingly. Typically, however, when killer whales are in the vicinity of humpbacks, the humpbacks react by becoming evasive, altering their course away from the killer whales, or remaining at a distance in a milling pattern. If the killers approach them, we have noticed that their respiration patterns change to less frequent exhalations, longer dive times and very subtle body movements. When the humpbacks are approached by killer whales, the exhalations reflect their agitation by becoming wheezed, a blow that indicates an excited whale.

125   Mountain goat with kid
Mother and kid watch us as we pass by.

126 Steller sea lion bulls *hauled out on Sunset Island. The large males weigh up to 2,200 pounds and reach a length of ten feet. Battle scars can be seen from the constant combats that occur between males over favored terrain. Steller sea lions are able to move on land by supporting their heavy bodies on their foreflippers and rotating their long flexible flippers (see pages 196-197).*

Killer whale attacks on humpbacks are rare. The sheer size of the humpback provides considerable immunity from the depredations of killer whales. Nonetheless, the distinctive scars caused by the interlocking teeth of the killer whale are seen on roughly 15 percent of the humpbacks in Alaska, usually on the flukes, dorsal fins and flippers. Killer whales use a number of predatory tactics to capture the large baleen whales, including a quiet stealthy approach to avoid detection. They have been seen using small bays in which to herd their quarry and to facilitate capture. In a particularly brazen act of hunting, killers in Argentina have been known to strand themselves temporarily in order to take seals and sea lions off the beach. Often they will divide up the task of subduing a large marine mammal, with some pod members holding the victim at bay by clamping onto the flukes or flippers, while other orcas rotate in and out to bite off chunks of its flesh. More frequently observed than actual attacks is the harassment of humpbacks. It is possible that killer whales harass humpbacks as a means of targeting out the more vulnerable individuals, such as young, old or sick whales.

We have witnessed two killer whale attacks on humpbacks in Southeast Alaska, both of which involved young whales. The first occurred in August 1983 while we were working from *Varua* in Frederick Sound. A juvenile humpback swam directly through an area where killers were attacking a bull Steller sea lion. The sea lion was badly wounded, with large bleeding gashes from the killer whale's teeth. The killers appeared to be more interested in tormenting the sea lion than in actually eating it, for they were tossing the 1200-pound bull around as if it were a ball, and only occasionally taking a chunk out of it. At this point, a juvenile humpback appeared, and foolishly approached close enough to distract the killers from the sea lion. Immediately they closed in on the humpback, charging toward it with tremendous speed, veering off, then charging in once again. Next, two adult humpbacks swam in to join the juvenile; they flanked it on both sides and defended it by slashing their flukes at the killer whales. The humpbacks also rolled over, so that their stomachs were above the water, perhaps to protect that delicate region from attack. They also lifted their flukes and chins out of the water simultaneously, possibly because the flukes, tongue and lips are reputably favored by the killer whales. This is a posture which we have also seen assumed by other humpbacks when in the presence of killer whales. Throughout the attack, we had a hydrophone in the water and recorded some humpback vocalizations and a great many killer whale sounds. One noteworthy sound was a very loud crash that we heard repeatedly. We believe that this occurred when a killer made contact with a humpback underwater, but we are unable to determine this conclusively. Eventually the killer whales divided up so that the bulls patrolled around the attack, while the females and young moved in to strike. When striking, a killer would leap into the air and come down on the whale, thrashing its tail violently, much as a shark does when tearing flesh. We did not at any time see blood or wounds on the humpbacks, yet there is no question that the killers repeatedly made contact.

The second attack we observed was from *Acania* in the summer of 1987 in Chatham Strait. Two killer whales suddenly appeared in the midst of a pod of humpbacks during a cooperative lunge feed. They targeted a calf for attack, but two adult humpbacks immediately sandwiched the calf between them, so forming a protective barrier. The calf was repeatedly raised partially out of the water by the flippers of the adults, who maintained this defensive formation for nearly 20 minutes until the killers departed. It appeared that the killers caught the humpbacks off guard, by using the humpback's feeding vocalization to mask their approach. When banded together in large cooperative feeding groups such as this one, humpbacks appear to be more vulnerable to surprise attack. The loud feeding vocalizations and surface commotion of cooperative groups can easily attract the attention of killer whales. When these animals move in to investigate a lunge feeding pod, our observations suggest that the typical humpback response is to stop feeding at once and disperse.

Two killer whales that have been sighted off the southern British Columbia coast (04 pod) have also been seen by us in Southeast Alaska. Our observations of these whales support the theory that transients may be more voracious meat eaters than residents. During an attack on Dall's porpoises in 1987, these two whales were seen leaping clear of the water and pouncing on their prey. Dall's porpoises are so small and fast that they seemed to be outmaneuvering the killers. By clearing the water with tremendous speed and coming down close to the porpoises, the killer whales could have seized the advantage and successfully attacked, had not a fishing boat interfered.

In every encounter we have observed between killer whales and humpbacks, either in playful harassment or determined effort, other humpbacks have come to the aid of the jeopardized animal, whether it be an adult or a juvenile. In a harassment observed in 1988 in Chatham Strait, humpbacks came from over a mile away to the aid of the victim. Such altruistic behavior is probably the humpbacks' best defense against the killer whale.

The loud, raucous complaints of Steller sea lion haulouts are a familiar sound of the Alaskan wilderness. Most of the pup rearing occurs on the outer coast, so these vociferous haulouts along the inside passages are primarily composed of males. Also known as the northern sea lion, the species is distinguished from the California sea lion by the brownish-yellow coat and large size. The males may exceed 2,000 pounds and 10 feet, this making them the largest of the eared seals. Sexual dimorphism is a characteristic of the sea lion, so that the females are smaller than the males, measuring 7 feet and 600 pounds. Steller sea lions, like other members of the family *Otariidae*, have the ability to rotate their long flexible hind flippers under the body and use their foreflippers for support. This gives them considerable mobility on land in comparison to seals, which do not support the body with their foreflippers, and look somewhat like undulating cigars when moving on land. Stellers are capable of climbing large boulders and traversing narrow ledges, to escape the crush of the colony. The clumsiness with which they move on land is lost when they enter the water. In that weightless medium they move with a wonderful grace and strength, as they propel themselves through the water with powerful strokes of the forelimbs, steering with their hind flippers clasped together.

The quarrelsome nature of Steller sea lions is readily evident from their constant bellowing and fighting on the haulouts as they defend their territories. On occasion, a humpback will swim too close to a haulout, and will immediately be attacked by the belligerent sea lions. On one such occasion over a dozen bulls stampeded into the water to attack a humpback that had approached the colony too closely. The sea lions nipped at the flukes and pectoral fins of the whale, while the whale used its appendages to slash back at the sea lions. These skirmishes sometimes last as long as an hour with the sea lions generally on the

127 Killer whale *A female killer whale at dusk prowls the deepwater channel of Chatham Strait. Residents are more apt to travel mid-channel in search of salmon while the transients, which tend to be more voracious meat eaters, often travel closer to shore in search of mammalian prey.*

offensive and the whale on the defensive. But one such "battle" that we observed between sea lions and a humpback calf may in fact have been boisterous play. If the sea lions swam off for a while, the calf would swim over to join them, rolling among them, following them for over a mile.

Although humpbacks are willing to joust with sea lions, lunge feeding groups show considerably less tolerance for them. The presence of a Steller sea lion can upset the delicate timing of a lunge feed, or disrupt a prey patch. An interfering sea lion invariably results in an aborted surfacing or temporary disaffiliation. Steller sea lions may have learned to associate group lunge feeding and the vocalization of whales with prolific prey, for we often see them working near cooperative pods. But these pods do not tolerate the intrusion, and will quickly respond to the sea lions with a tail slash or pec slap. It is doubtful that they ever seriously hurt each other, but sea lions nipping at a humpback's appendages may be the cause of some of the nicks and scars that adorn the tail flukes.

CONCLUSION

The previous pages have described one of the rarest
animals on earth from the perspective of scientific fact. Yet
objective and didactic treatment tells only half the story. I
do not believe it possible to work with an animal so
graceful and majestic as the humpback whale without
developing an existential awareness that cannot be
described on a data sheet. For as long as we have had
records, man has expressed a belief in a mystical bond with
dolphins and whales. Unravelling the mysteries of these
creatures works only to strengthen that bond. The study of
whales is romantic and exciting work, even though difficult
and tedious at times and unexpectedly dangerous at others.
The scientific analysis of our observations must always be
extremely precise, but it should always be enlightened by
an open mind, sensitive to the apprehension of something
that exists far beyond our human understanding. Therein
lies the key to the ultimate protection of these animals.
Scientific documentation is essential, and accurate data
collection is a part of science. But it is the response of our
imaginations, and the challenge that our knowledge of the
whales presents to our anthropocentric view of life, that
offers them their best chance of survival in a world

128 *Acania* in the afternoon.

otherwise dominated by our all too human concern for fast
material gain.

The extensive whaling of the twentieth century has
brought the humpback whale near to extinction. We have
said that at the turn of the century there were
approximately 120,000 humpbacks in the world, and that
now there are only about 10,000. In the North Pacific,
before exploitation began, there were some 15,000. Now
there remains only one in ten, a mere 1,500 approximate
North Pacific population.

Since 1972 the United States Marine Mammal
Protection Act has brought the humpback some relief from

being hunted, but the population remains low. Why has this species had such a slow recovery rate, when the gray whales have regained their original numbers and then some? Perhaps it is because the humpback's calving grounds are subject to such intense interaction with humans. What if this were to occur on their feeding grounds, as well? Alaska's waterways are becoming much more popular, both for tourism and industry. It is therefore increasingly important that we assess the impact of different stimuli on the humpbacks, and gather more information about their behavior, so that changes can be monitored and, when necessary, made.

Our research on the cooperative feeding of humpbacks offers us another hypothesis as to why their recovery rate is low. During the whaling years, the largest whales, which were also the oldest, were favored targets. The killing of the elders, and of a high percentage of adults, may have destroyed valuable survival information, such as the cooperative feeding technique. If critical knowledge of this technique and others were lost the humpback whale, as a species that survives on highly sophisticated strategies in obtaining prey, could well be so disadvantaged that its population growth is being affected. Over the past eight years we have noted a marked increase in the number of groups cooperatively feeding. This may reflect the gradual recovery of a strategic feeding maneuver that is gaining participants every year, or it could reflect a shift in prey distribution, or it may be a comment on our own observational techniques, despite their careful employment. But each year calves actively participate in the cooperative groups, adding to the membership. In 1988 we saw juveniles participating that were calves we had seen the previous year. In addition ten new calves were sighted by 1st July 1988, the latest additions to the cooperative lunge feeding pods. We are therefore certain that the membership of cooperative pods is growing annually, which leaves us with an optimistic perspective on the outlook of the humpback. Future studies will enable us to interpret the growth of this behavior accurately, as well as

129 *Varua* crossing Chatham Strait.

to answer some questions about the leadership of cooperative groups. The answer to these questions, among others, may give us clues about the role of learning, as compared to instinct, and may ultimately address the issue of what affects the rate of survival.

Our studies of cooperatively feeding pods have also opened up entirely new avenues of thought regarding mysticete whales. The fact that humpback whales are capable of cooperating indicates a higher level of intelligence, such as has until now been chiefly credited to the toothed whales. That there are specific leaders, which are generally the largest whales, and that there is probably a social hierarchy governing this precise maneuver, opens a new perspective for understanding the social relationships of humpbacks. The choreography of the coordinated maneuver is very exacting. It hardly seems possible that, at 80,000 pounds each, as many as 22 whales could maneuver in such a tight area under such precise constraints. Their ability to do so is a tribute not only to their grace, but to a sophistication that rivals, indeed surpasses, the most complex odontocete feeding behaviors. However, many of the points addressed here will require further investigation before any final conclusions are reached. For example, just how an entire aggregation of humpbacks can detect a prolific feeding area over a hundred miles away, and determine that it will be better to depart the moderately rewarding area in which they are already, is only one of the questions we shall be better equipped to answer as we learn more about their finely tuned sensitivity and their incredibly complex interactions with the environment.

Humpbacks are known for their beautiful, complex songs while on the winter grounds, yet their reason for singing is still subject to speculation. The songs have never been associated with a specific behavior, or related conclusively to an individual whale. The songs we have been recording on the feeding grounds are the first to have been associated directly with a specific behavior. This offers evidence that the singing is not casual, but has a definite purpose. It is interesting that the song on the winter calving grounds undergoes annual changes, while the feeding song remains the same from year to year in the case of specific individuals, though different from group to group. A natural question is why each group would have a different song. Perhaps it is that each leader develops its own song, and this acts as a means of identification, like a signature. This may explain why there is duetting on some occasions, when two leaders are in the same temporary pod. On the other hand, it may also provide a means of establishing territories. When a number of cooperative pods are working the same general area, the song may eliminate confusion by delineating boundaries. Also it may well be that extraneous information is being communicated in the feeding song, aside from attracting whales to the group. Again these questions can be better addressed over time. But the fact that an individual whale, feeding alone, will use the vocalization, suggests that at least one purpose of the song may be to control the prey. The fact that a calf is capable of singing the song, though the pattern is not yet well developed, and that the calf can blow a bubble net, and actively feed on its own while employing these highly evolved techniques, shows how quickly a humpback is capable of learning. If the calves are still nursing at the end of a year, they are without a doubt heavily supplementing their diet by feeding independently while on the Alaskan feeding grounds.

Researchers have debated whether mysticete groupings should rightly be considered "pods", because the baleen whales have been thought to form only temporary affiliations—the term pod having been defined by some cetologists as an enduring association, such as the family groupings of killer whales. Whether or not that debate can be finally settled, the long-term affiliations we have seen among some humpbacks offer the first evidence that mysticetes do form lasting associations that endure over years. In 1988 Mama and Rake, who have been seen together since 1983, were seen with a calf. Perhaps there are family units as have been determined among some of the toothed whales.

Our nighttime feeding studies are still in their infancy, but they have positively identified the humpback as an active feeder in total darkness. This provides additional clues into the unique methodology of humpback feeding. By studying the humpback's different feeding strategies, and by learning the reasons for their use, we can learn more about their needs and therefore better understand the ways in which they are vulnerable. For instance, if the sound made by the herring is an essential element of successful cooperative feeding, what would be the result of heavy vessel traffic in critical feeding areas? Is the sound of large ships enough to mask the feeding vocalization, and make it ineffective, or perhaps even more importantly would the sound affect the herring so that cooperative feeding would not be possible? Schools of herring are very sensitive to the accelerated approach of a small boat, or to the loud, low-frequency throbbing created by larger vessels. These disturbing sounds can alter the flight response of herring, and could result in depriving the humpbacks of their hard-sought-after meal. With increased observations we may be able to learn more of the effects of vessel traffic on subtle behaviors, both of the prey and of the whales.

By working both extremes of the migration, in northern feeding and southern calving grounds, we are able to document changes in basic behaviors. Identifying individuals and comparing associations will give us a great deal of insight into their social structure. We now have two ships from which to conduct our studies, which makes these studies infinitely more feasible. Of particular interest to us will be the comparison of singers and songs between the winter calving and summer feeding grounds.

Though these future discoveries are already within our grasp, our curiosity is now extending beyond Alaskan and Hawaiian humpback studies to comparisons of humpbacks in both Northern and Southern Hemispheres. *Varua* will return to the South Seas, her home of 30 years, to continue the studies on Southern Hemisphere cetaceans which we began in the latter part of the 1970s. We shall be making behavioral and anatomical comparisons and conducting a census of local aggregations. We shall also be comparing the vocalizations between the two extremes. After every study, new insights are achieved; yet for every question answered, more questions arise. The pool of knowledge is expanding, however, as researchers around the world collaborate on their findings.

We have brought together in this book the most frequently observed behaviors of the humpback in an effort to make that mysterious animal better known to all. Though we have been working with humpback whales for many years, we never cease to learn new aspects of their complex and subtle behavior, nor does respect and admiration for the wonder of these magnificent creatures ever diminish. Yet there is only so much we can do to save them. Scientists alone do not hold the key to the preservation of the seas and their inhabitants. This will require an awareness on the part of thinking, informed and caring people, in every society that impinges upon the humpback whales, and upon the fragile waters in which they live.

130 Flukes at dawn (right)

GLOSSARY

BIBLIOGRAPHY

INDEX

GLOSSARY

aborted surfacing: occurs when a pod dives and begins the feeding call, but subsequently abandons the pursuit and surfaces in a normal non-lunge surfacing

affiliation: when a pod or individuals join together

ascending vocalization: the last few phrases of the feeding vocalization which rise in frequency; given as the pod is rushing toward the surface

baleen: the two rows of plates that hang from each side of the mouth, used to filter out prey organisms, also called whale bone

breach: the leap of a whale above the surface of the water, typically landing with a large splash

bubble net: a ring of bubbles created by emitting air out of the blowhole, aids in the capture of fish

caudal peduncle: the tail stock of a whale

cooperative lunge feeding: the synchronous lunging of a group of humpbacks through the surface during the pursuit of prey

disaffiliation: occurs when members of a pod depart

dorsal: the topside of a whale

dorsal fin: the small appendage on the back of whales that acts as a stabilizer while swimming

dive profile: the pattern in which a whale or pod dives; the recording of a whale's dive profile requires measuring the length of time the whale is submerged, the length of time spent on the surface, the number of spouts per surfacing, and similar information

euphausiid: a small shrimp-like crustacean often referred to as krill

feeding vocalization: the loud, low-frequency call used by humpbacks to manipulate schools of small agile fish

flipper: the forelimbs of a marine mammal

fluke up dive: arching the tail and caudal peduncle high into the air to gain momentum at the beginning of a dive, permits viewing of the unique pigmentation pattern on the underside of the flukes

flukes: the tail of a whale

hydrophone: a microphone used for monitoring underwater sounds

krill: a small shrimp-like crustacean (*euphausiid*) that constitutes the major part of the diet of several species of baleen whales

lateral lunge feed: plowing through prey parallel to the surface with mouth agape, frequently performed rolled over onto the right side

lunge formation: the physical orientation and positioning that each whale adopts when lunging through the surface

Megaptera novaeangliae: the scientific or latin name of the humpback whale, meaning "big-winged New Englander"

pectoral fin: the flippers or forelimbs of a marine mammal

pectoral fin slap: hitting the surface of the water with a flipper, usually creating a loud noise and large splash

peduncle slap: slap with the tail stock of a whale

percussionary activity: generating sound by striking the surface with the flukes, pectoral fins, or body

primary call: the main phrases of the feeding vocalization

sensory nodules: the large bumps that adorn the face and pectoral fins of a humpback, believed to aid in sensing the environment

song: fixed patterns of repeated sounds

sonic scattering layer: the horizons of krill and other small marine organisms that can be detected with echo sounders or fathometers

sounding: submerging after a series of blows, usually with a fluke-up dive

spyhop: the slow vertical rise of a whale out of the water until the eyes are at a level to peer at objects above the surface

trumpet blow: a loud airborne sound that is produced in the blowhole while the whale is at the surface; uncommon and usually performed by whales in a highly excited or stressful emotional state

ventral region: the underside of a whale

vertical lunge feed: hurtling straight up out of the water with mouth agape

vibrisal: from *vibrissae*, the stiff coarse hairs or whiskers found near the mouths of most mammals

water column: occurs when bodies of water move up and down to create vertical flows

wheezed blow: a loud, emphatic exhalation produced by constricting the nostrils, given by excited whales

SELECTED BIBLIOGRAPHY

Baker C.D. 1985. "The population structure and social organization of humpback whales (*Megaptera novaeangliae*) in the Central and Eastern North Pacific." Doctoral Thesis, Univ. of Hawaii, Honolulu.

Broughton W.B. 1963. *Acoustic Behavior of Animals*. R.G. Busnel, Ed. (Elsevier, London), pp. 824-910.

Brueggeman J.J., G.A. Green, R.A. Grotefendt, and D.G. Chapman. 1987. "Humpback whale abundance and distribution off the Alaskan Peninsula. Seventh Biennial Conference on the Biology of Marine Mammals." Abstracts.

Bryant P.J., G. Nichols, T.B. Bryant, and K. Miller. 1981. "Krill availability and the distribution of humpback whales in Southeast Alaska." *J. Mamm.* 62(2):427-430.

Cubbage J.C., J. Calambokidis, K.C. Balcomb, and J. Steiger. 1987. "Humpback whale (*Megaptera novaeangliae*) distribution and abundance in the Gulf of the Farallones, California." Seventh Biennial Conference on the Biology of Marine Mammals. Abstracts.

D'Vincent, C.G, R.M. Nilson, and R. H. Hanna. 1985. "Vocalization and coordinated feeding behavior of the humpback whale *(Megaptera novaeangliae)* in southeastern Alaska." Sci. Rep. Whales Res. Inst. 36:41-47.

D'Vincent C.G, R.M. Nilson, and F.A. Sharpe. 1988. "Observations of humpback whale (*Megaptera novaeangliae*) mother-calf pairs in Southeast Alaska," in *Cetus, The Journal of Whales, Porpoises and Dolphins*. 8(1):25-27.

Darling J.D., and C.M. Jurasz. 1983. "Migratory destinations of the North Pacific humpback whale (*Megaptera novaeangliae*)," in R. Payne (editor), *Communication and Behavior of Whales*, Westview Press, Boulder, Co. pp. 359-368.

Dolphin W.F. 1986. "Dive behavior and estimated energy expenditure of foraging humpback whales in Southeast Alaska." *Can. J. Zool.* 65:354-362.

Dolphin W.F. 1987. "Ventilation and dive patterns of humpback whale (*Megaptera novaeangliae*) on their Alaskan feeding grounds." *Can. J. Zool.* 65:83-90.

Dolphin W.F. 1987. "Prey densities and foraging of humpback whales (*Megaptera novaeangliae*)." *Experientia 43*, Birkahuser Veriag, CH-4010 Basel/Switzerland.

Gaskin D.E. 1976. The evolution, zoogeography and ecology of Cetacea. Ann. Rev. Oceanogr. Mar. Biol. 14:247-346

Hain J.W., et.al. 1982. "Feeding behavior of the humpback whale (*Megaptera novaeangliae)* in the Western North Atlantic." *Fishery Bulletin.* 80:259-268.

Hafner G.W., et al. 1979. Signature information in the song of the humpback whale. *J. Acoust. Soc. Am.* 66(1), July 1979.

Hall J.D. 1979. "A survey of cetaceans of Prince William Sound and adjacent vicinity—their numbers and seasonal movements." Pages 631-726, "Environmental assessment of the Alaskan continental shelf." Final Reports to the Principal Investigators, Volume 6, *Biological Studies*, NOAA-OCSEAP, Boulder, CO.

Hay K.A. 1985. "Status of the Humpback Whale, *(Megaptera novaeangliae)* in Canada," *Can. Field Naturalist.* 99(3):425-432.

International Whaling Commission. "Behavior of whales in relationship to management, 1986, incorporating the proceedings of a workshop of the same name, held in Seattle, Washington, 19-32, April, 1982." Edited by Gregory P. Donovan. Special Issue 8, *Report of the International Whaling Commission.* Cambridge, Mass. p.17.

Jurasz C.M., and V.P. Jurasz. 1979. "Feeding modes of the humpback whale (*Megaptera novaeangliae*) in Southeast Alaska." Sci. Rep. Whales Res. Inst. 31:69-83.

Krieger K., and B.L. Wing. 1986. "Hydroacoustic monitoring of prey to determine humpback whale movements." U.S. Department of Commerce, NOAA Technical Memorandum NMFS F/NWC-98:62.

Major P.F., L.M. Dill, and D.M. Eaves. 1986. "Three-dimensional predator-prey interactions: a computer simulation of bird flocks and aircraft." *Can. J. Zool.* 64:2624-2633.

National Marine Fisheries Service. 1986. "Marine Mammal Protection Act of 1972." U.S. Department of Commerce, NMFS Washington D.C.

Nemoto T. 1970. "The feeding pattern of baleen whales in the ocean." Pages 241-381 in J.H. Steele, (editor). *Marine food chains*. Oliver and Boyd, Edinburgh.

Norris K.S., and T.P. Dohl. 1980. *Cetacean Behavior: Mechanisms and function* (pp.211-261) Wiley. New York.

Ovenholtz W.J., and J.R. Nicolas. 1979. "Apparent feeding by the fin whale, *(Balaenoptera physalus)*, and the humpback whale (*Megaptera novaeangliae*) on the American Sand Lance (*Ammodytes americanus*), in the northwest Atlantic." *Fish. Bull.* 77(1):285-278.

Payne R.S., and S. McVay. 1971. Songs of humpback whales. *Science.* 173:585-597.

Robinson W.A. 1972. *Return to the Sea*. Peter Davies Limited, London.

Robinson W.A. 1956. *To the Great Southern Sea*. John De Graff, Inc., Tuckahoe, NY.

Scammon C.M. 1874. *The marine mammals of the northwestern coast of North America: together with an account of the American whale-fishery*. San Francisco: John H Carmany and Co. (Reprinted 1968 in paperback. Dover. New York.

Randall S.W., B.A. Irviene, and M.D. Scott. 1980. *The social ecology of inshore odontocetes. The structure and function of cetacean schools*. Wiley. New York.

Schwarz A.L., and G.L. Greer. 1984. "Response of pacific herring (*Clupea harengus pallasi*) to some underwater sounds." *Can. J. Fish* Aquatic Sci. 41:1183-1192.

Tyack P. 1981. Interactions between singing Hawaiian humpback whales and conspecifics nearby. *Behav. Ecol. and Sociobiol.* 8:105-116.

Tyack P., and H. Whitehead. 1983. "Male competition in large groups of wintering humpback whales." *Behavior* 83:132-154.

Urban J., K.C. Balcomb, C. Alvarez, P. Bloedel, J. Cubbage, J. Calambokidis, and G. Steiger. 1987. "Photo-identification matches of humpback whales *(Megaptera novaeangliae)* between Mexico and Central California." Seventh Biennial Conference on the Biology of Marine Mammals. Abstracts.

Von Ziegesar O. 1984. "A survey of the humpback whales in southwestern Prince William Sound, Alaska 1980, 1981, and 1983." *A Report to the State of Alaska: Alaska Council on Science & Technology*. North Gulf Oceanic Society, Cordova, Alaska.

Watkins W.A., and W.E. Schevill. 1979. Aerial observation of feeding behavior in four baleen whales: *Eubalaena glacialis, Balaenoptera borealis, Megaptera novaeangliae, and Balaenoptera physalus*. 60(1):155-163.

Whitehead H., and C. Glass. 1985. "Orcas (killer whales) attack humpback whales." *Journal of Mammology.* 66(1):183–185.

Winn H.E., et al. 1981. Song of the humpback whale—population comparisons. *Behav. Ecol. Sociobiol.* 8:41-46.

INDEX

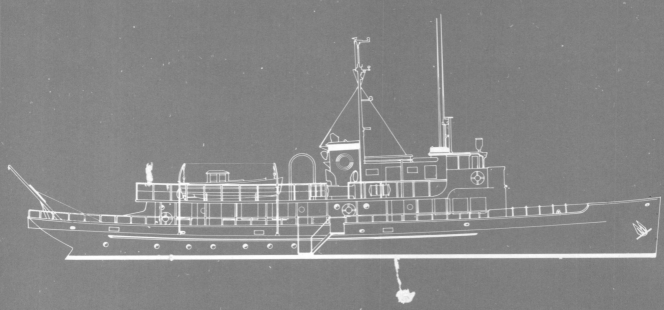